Basic Science Questions
for Key Stage 4

in 2 volumes

Basic Science Questions for Key Stage 4

B. J. Rouan and B. C. Abrams

Book 2

Stanley Thornes (Publishers) Ltd

First published in 1991 by
Stanley Thornes (Publishers) Ltd
Old Station Drive
Leckhampton
CHELTENHAM GL53 0DN
England

The cover shows a false-colour bubble chamber photograph of the tracks of subatomic particles, and is reproduced by permission of Patrice Loiez, Cern/Science Photo Library.

British Library Cataloguing in Publication Data
Rouan, B. J.
  Basic science questions for key stage 4.
  1. Science
  I. Title   II. Abrams, B. C.
  500

ISBN 0–7487–0556–2 Book 1
ISBN 0–7487–0592–9 Book 2

Typeset by Tech-Set, Gateshead, Tyne & Wear.
Printed and bound in Great Britain at The Bath Press, Avon.

Contents – Book 2

Topic 6: Information Technology, Electronics and Microelectronics 163

Topic 7: The Nature of Science 187

Contents – Book 1

Topic 1: Investigating Science 1

Topic 2: Life Science 15

Preface

With the introduction of the National Curriculum, pressures on science teachers are considerable and increasing. There is more demand than ever for exercises that are instructive, easy to correct and evaluate, and which are consistent with the latest curriculum reforms.

These books have been written to reinforce the basic science required by modern syllabuses and to address National Curriculum Programmes of Study for Science. By incorporating a wide variety of question styles, students can acquire the knowledge, understanding and skills required by GCSE examinations. To help students develop a clear overall view of the subject, and to understand the development of ideas and concepts, we have included questions based on Key Stage 3 material. The questions have been written for use with students of a wide range of ability.

In addition to providing a framework within which students can compile a useful set of accurate notes, alone or with the help of a teacher, this book can be used to monitor students' progress. It can also form the basis for a comprehensive revision programme – recent examination questions have been included.

Although there are questions asking students to copy diagrams, we expect that in many cases they will be traced.

Barbara Rouan
Bernard Abrams
Cheltenham 1991

Acknowledgements

The authors and publisher are grateful to Ian Ward, Pan Books Ltd and Penguin Books Ltd for permission to use the extracts on pp. 13, 21 and 190 respectively, and the following for permission to reproduce examination questions:

London East Anglian Group
Midland Examining Group
Northern Examining Association
Southern Examining Group
Welsh Joint Education Committee

Many people have helped in the production of this book, and we would like to thank colleagues for their constructive criticisms of the questions. Finally it is our pleasure to thank our publishers Stanley Thornes, and all those involved in the design and production of this book.

Every effort has been made to contact copyright holders, and we apologise to any we have not been able to reach.

TOPIC 4

Earth, Atmosphere and Space

4.1 EARTH AND ATMOSPHERE

4.1.1 Rocks, Soils and Minerals

1   What can be learnt from a study of

a)   rock texture?

b)   rock colour(s)?

2   Two students were asked to compare the ability of two samples of limestone to absorb water. The methods they chose are outlined in the table.

Emma	*Steven*
1. Take 1 cm³ cube of each type of limestone.	1. Take two 10.0 g samples of each type of limestone.
2. Put 50.0 cm³ water in each of two measuring cylinders.	2. Place each sample in a beaker containing 50.0 cm³ water.
3. Put one sample of limestone in each measuring cylinder.	3. After 20 minutes, remove each sample and re-weigh.
4. Note the new volume reading on the measuring cylinders after 5 minutes.	4. Calculate the gain in mass of each sample.

a)   For each method state

  i) one source of inaccuracy

  ii) how the accuracy of the result could be improved

b)   How would Emma use her results to decide which sample was more absorbent?

c)   Jane noticed that one of Steven's samples had broken into two fragments. Would this affect the result of the experiment? Explain your answer.

d)   Two samples of another sedimentary rock, sandstone, are shown below. Which would you expect to be more absorbent and why?

Specimen A   Specimen B

3   Pair these groups of words to form sentences about soil:

a) **Soil is formed from rock**   in colour than subsoil.

b) **Weathering agents include**   remains of dead organisms, called humus.

c) **Topsoil is generally darker**   important for plant growth.

d) **Topsoil contains decaying**   rain, wind, snow and frost.

e) **If a sample of soil is shaken in water and allowed to stand**   gravel, humus, mineral salts, water and air.

f) **The finest particles of soil are**   by the action of weathering agents.

g) **Soil contains sand, clay,**   nitrogen, phosphorus, potassium and magnesium.

h) **Mineral salts in soil water are**   filled with air and water.

i) **The kind and amount of minerals in soil depend on**   the type of rock the soil was formed from and the activities of bacteria.

j) **Some important elements in mineral salts are**   clay particles with a diameter less than 0.002 mm.

k) **Spaces between the soil particles are**   the larger particles settle first.

4   Explain the importance of the following components of the soil:

a) humus   b) lime   c) mineral salts   d) soil water   e) soil air

5   A sample of soil was placed in a tall glass measuring cylinder with a large volume of water. It was then shaken and left to settle completely. The results are shown in this diagram:

a) Copy the diagram and replace the letters A–F with correct labels.

b) Which soil particles settle first and why?

c) Why does part B appear cloudy?

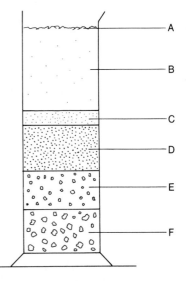

6 Below are seven pairs of statements about soil. Construct a table with two headings like the one below. For each pair of descriptions, decide which one applies to sandy soil and which one to clay soil; then complete the table.

Sandy soil	Clay soil

a) Composed mainly of large particles
    Composed mainly of fine particles

b) Contains large air spaces
    Contains small air spaces

c) Poorly drained and aerated
    Well drained and aerated

d) Useful chemicals are washed out when it rains
    Holds on to useful chemicals well

e) Rich in plant food
    Poor in plant food

f) Loose, light and easy to dig
    Cold, heavy and difficult to dig

7 An analysis of two soil samples carried out by a gardener gave the following results:

	Sample A	Sample B
Sand	85%	22%
Clay	14%	70%
Humus	1%	8%

a) Give *one* advantage and *one* disadvantage of each soil sample for growing young plants.

b) How could you improve soil from sample A so that plants would grow better in it?

c) How could you improve soil of type B?

d) The ideal garden soil is called **loam**.
    i) What, roughly, should its composition be?
    ii) Why is loam better for plant growth than sandy or clay soil?

e) i) Why is peaty soil not very fertile?
    ii) Why is it improved by adding lime?

f) Why is chalky soil alkaline?

8 a) Earthworms live in the soil. Describe *four* ways in which the earthworm is useful to gardeners.

b) Name *two* soil organisms which are pests and say why they are pests.

9 The diagram below shows a landscape that is being altered by water, wind, ice, temperature change and by plant roots. Look at the diagram and answer the questions which follow.

a) Describe *two* ways in which the cliff could be broken down.

b) i) What is a glacier?

ii) Suggest *two* ways that the movement of ice down the glacier would affect the rock that it is in contact with.

iii) Why are rock particles deposited at the foot of the glacier?

c) Pick out *one* other place where rock is being broken down and explain how this happens.

d) How are rock particles carried to the sea?

e) What sort of rock will eventually be formed as layer after layer of rock particles are deposited on the bed of the lake?

f) The mountains are found to be made of a very hard igneous rock which has large crystals in it. Describe how this rock would have been formed.

10 a) Explain how each of the following can produce soil erosion:
   i) deforestation
   ii) overgrazing
   iii) bad agricultural practices

  b) Suggest ways of reducing soil erosion.

11

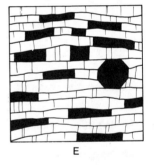

Use the key provided to identify the rock specimens A–E above.

1. Does the rock show a 'mosaic' pattern of crystals, or *appear* to have fragments of one material embedded in another?	Crystal mosaic – go to 4 Fragments – go to 2
2. Are the fragments aligned?	Yes – SCHIST No – go to 3
3. Does the rock appear coarse or fine-grained?	Course – GABRO Fine – ORTHOQUARTZITE
4. Are there crystals of more than one mineral?	Yes – GRANITE No – METAQUARTZITE

12   The diagram shows the rock structure under part of England.

Write down the letters of the rocks shown in the key which are *younger* than chalk. Explain your answer.

13

The diagram above shows the layers of rock beneath a well.

a)   Give *one* origin of the underground water.

b)   Name *one* sedimentary and *one* igneous rock shown in the diagram.

c)   i) What is meant by 'hard water'?
     ii) Would you expect water drawn from this well to be hard or soft? Explain your answer.

d)   Describe *one* problem caused by hard water in the home.

14   Under the Earth's crust there is hot, molten rock. In some places water drains down
to the hot rocks above the molten material and is sent back up again as a geyser or as a
hot spring. The energy from these springs is used in some countries such as Iceland.
The diagram below shows the typical geological structure of an area where hot
springs might occur.

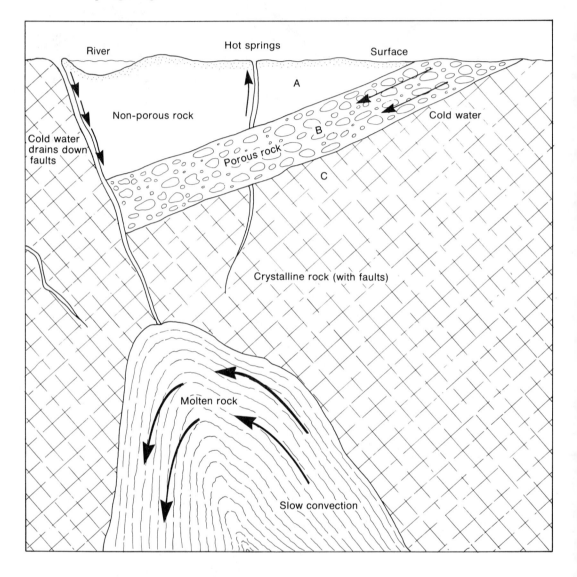

a)   i) Which one of the rocks labelled A, B and C is most likely to be igneous?
Give *one* reason for your choice.

ii) Suggest *one* cause of the fault lines shown in the diagram.

b)   Britain does not have any natural geysers but artificial geysers have been made.
Two bore-holes are drilled down into the rocks. Cold water enters by one hole
and returns to the surface at a higher temperature (see next page).

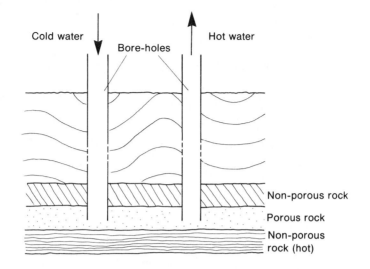

For every kilometre you go below the surface the temperature rises by as much as 40 °C.

i) Assuming that the water pumped in is at 10 °C, what is the minimum depth the bore-holes need to go to, to heat the water to 90 °C?

ii) Explain why the water reaching the surface will be at a lower temperature than 90 °C.

iii) This method could be used to produce steam to drive a turbine-generator. Suggest why this might make the production of electricity cheaper.

15 The diagram shows part of the rock cycle.

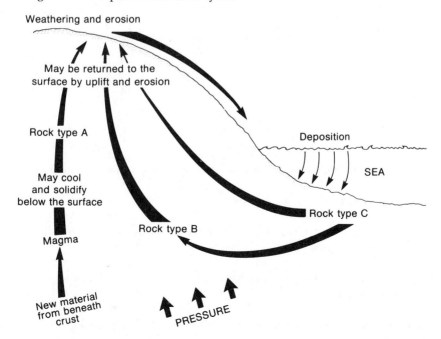

a) What names are given to the three types of rock, A, B and C, shown in the diagram?

b) Suggest *two* features you would expect sedimentary rocks to have.

c) Suggest *two* conditions necessary to convert sedimentary rocks to metamorphic rocks.

d) Suggest *two* methods by which rocks at the surface might be weathered.

16

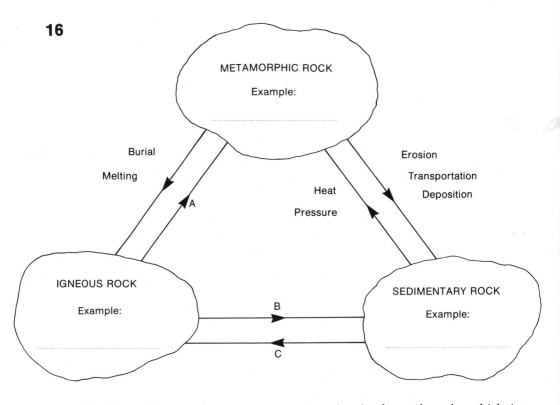

The above diagram shows processes occurring in the rock cycle, which inter-convert the three types of rock.

a) Copy the diagram and add the processes which are missing at A, B and C.

b) Add the name of one example of each type of rock.

c) Explain what the words **erosion, transportation** and **deposition** mean as applied to the rock cycle.

d) Why are sedimentary rocks more likely to be metamorphosed than igneous rocks?

e) Name the two major driving forces for change within the rock cycle.

17   Some chemical elements decay with age, producing radioactivity in the process. Potassium turns into argon, and rubidium into strontium. Uranium-238 is an element which decays through a series of radioactive products to finish as lead-206. In any uranium ore the proportion of lead-206 increases with time. The decay occurs at a constant rate, the half-life of uranium-238 being 4 500 000 000 years.

Explain briefly how scientists can use this information to determine the age of rocks.

4.1.2 Earthquakes and Volcanoes

1   The map shows the location of two regions of granite in Scotland. It is believed that they were once part of a single granite mass. Movement of rock masses along a fault line slowly separated the two samples.

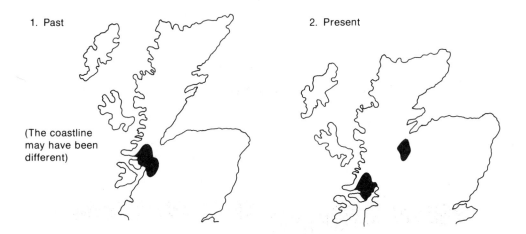

1. Past

2. Present

(The coastline may have been different)

a)   Trace map number 2 and draw on it the fault line responsible for the separation. Add arrows to indicate the direction of movement on each side of the fault.

b)   Choose a timescale from those listed below in which this change is likely to have occurred.

            5 years   **5000 years**   **5 million years**

c)   The distance between the granite locations today is approximately 100 km. Using your answer to part b), calculate the average rate of displacement in centimetres per year.

d)   What causes displacements such as this?

2

Sloping fault plane

Stage 1   ➝   Stage 2   ➝   Stage 3

The diagrams show three stages in the evolution of the land near a fault zone.

a) In stage 1, were the rocks on each side of the fault under compression or tension? Explain your answer.

b) Describe the changes which have occurred between stages 2 and 3, and give two possible causes.

c) Draw a diagram, equivalent to stage 3, showing one possible outcome when the forces acting on the rocks are in the opposite direction to those in this example.

d) What is the origin of the forces which caused the movement?

3

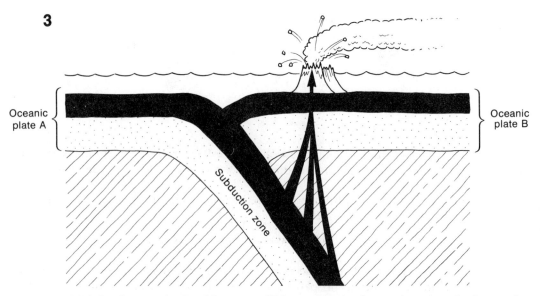

Oceanic plate A

Oceanic plate B

Subduction zone

Mobile plates in the Earth's crust collide as a result of tectonic action. At destructive plate margins, crust is forced downwards in a subduction zone. In the example shown, two oceanic plates are involved.

a) In which direction is each of the plates moving?

b) Give *two* reasons why rock forced downwards into a subduction zone is likely to melt, leading to volcanism.

c) What would be found above a subduction zone where two continental plates are colliding?

d) What is believed to be the driving force for tectonic action?

4 The article reproduced below appeared in *The Daily Telegraph* of 26th September, 1984. Read the article carefully and answer the questions which follow.

VOLCANO ASH DIMS SUNLIGHT

By IAN WARD in Manila

A SIX MILE-HIGH dense cloud of ash hung yesterday over the entire southern Luzon province of Albay, where the Mayon volcano continues its spectacular display.

Thousands fled villages threatened by flows of lava and mud.

The aerial blanket of ash transformed the noon sky over the province into a murky half-light as farmers

around the volcano abandoned vast stretches of rice fields now lying under large layers of mud.

Philippine Airlines removed all jets from its southern Luzon schedules, replacing them with propeller-driven aircraft as a safety precaution against airborne volcanic ash, which can quickly snuff out jet engines.

Boulders big as cars

The Philippine Civil Aviation Authority continued to warn foreign commercial aircraft to fly clear of the ash clouds, which were drifting in several directions from the erupting crater, but have been meticulously plotted by satellite technology.

Throughout the day Mayon hurled boulders as big as cars into the air and down its slopes. To add to the awesome display flashes of lightning repeatedly hit the top of the belching cone of the volcano.

But vulcanologists said seismic readings were now suggesting that the worst of the eruption, which began with a huge blast on September 9, was over.

Many evacuees have been treated for burns and lung problems associated with inhalation of gases and ash, but no deaths have been reported as a result of the volcano's present eruption.

a) Why did the population flee from their valleys?

b) Why were jets forbidden from flying near the volcanic eruption?

c) The eruption produced liquid, solid and gaseous materials.

   i) Name *one* solid and *one* liquid which were thrown out.

   ii) Name *one* gas which escapes from a volcano.

5   The map below shows part of the world with plate boundaries and plate movement indicated.

----- Plate boundaries

a)   Trace the map and add labels to indicate one constructive and one destructive plate margin.

b)   At which of the sites A, B or C would you expect to find
   i)   volcanism?
   ii) mountain building?

6

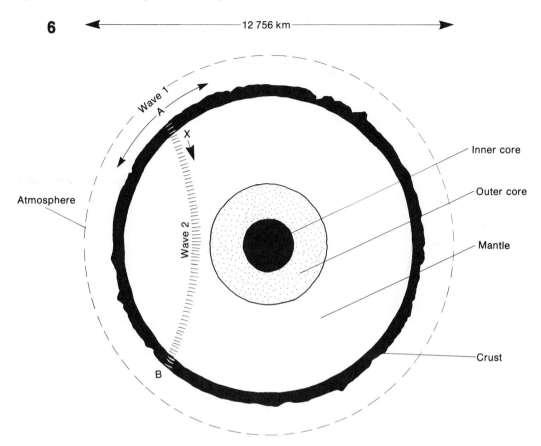

The diagram (not to scale) shows the layered internal structure of the Earth. An earthquake occurring at X, directly below the epicentre (A), is detected at location B. Shock waves arrive at B over a period of 15 minutes.

a) What name is given to point X?

b) Which wave is a P wave?

c) An earthquake occurs when forces inside the Earth cause large masses of rock to fracture and move. Waves from the Earthquake travel through the Earth and along the crust.

   i) Explain why the wave travelling through the Earth takes a curved path.

   ii) Give two reasons why waves travelling along the crust take longer to reach location B than those travelling through the mantle.

   iii) Would you expect earthquakes to originate below a depth of 1000 km? Explain your answer.

d) Suggest one result of a major earthquake occurring beneath the sea.

e) Give two pieces of information which suggest that the Earth has a core containing iron.

4.1.3 **Weather**

1   The following symbols are used on weather maps and charts. Explain what each symbol represents.

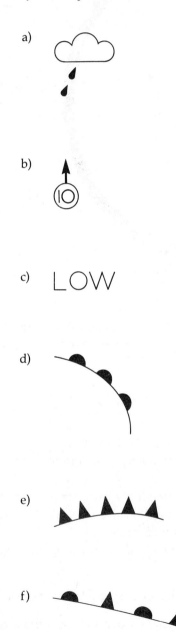

a)

b)

c)   LOW

d)

e)

f)

2 Kalpesh recorded the temperature on one day every week for a year. The readings were taken at midday, and were used to calculate the mean (average) temperature for each month as shown in the table below.

Month	Mean temperature (°C)
January	−2.0
February	+2.5
March	+6.0
April	+10.0
May	+14.0
June	+16.5
July	+20.0
August	+19.0
September	+14.5
October	+10.5
November	+5.0
December	+1.5

a) i) Use the results in the table to plot a column graph showing the temperature variation over the year.

ii) Does Kalpesh live in the northern or southern hemisphere? Explain your answer.

b) Alan, another of the students in Kalpesh's class, carried out similar measurements and produced the following bar graph.

Mean temperature/°C

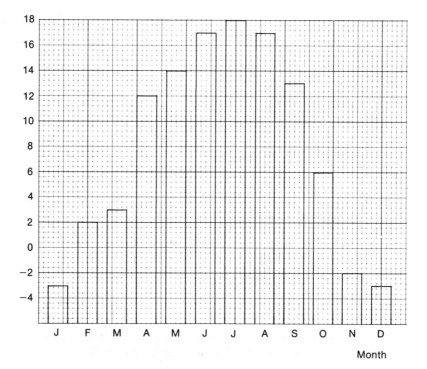

Month

   i) Explain why Alan's readings can be different to Kalpesh's without being
      wrong.

   ii) How could the accuracy of both sets of results be improved?

c) Copy and complete the following table.

	Kalpesh	*Alan*
Month with the highest mean temperature		
Month with the lowest mean temperature		
Mean temperature for the whole year		

3

10 June   5 December

The two weather maps show the isobar pattern over north-west Europe at two
different times of year. All other symbols (except HIGH and LOW) have been
removed.

a) What does an isobar represent?

b) In each case, predict the direction and strength of the winds over Great Britain.

c) Using the information on the maps, describe the weather conditions in Britain on
   i) 10 June
   ii) 5 December

4 a) Explain the difference between climate and weather.

   b) The climate graphs following are for different places in the world. Look at the
      graphs and answer the questions which follow.

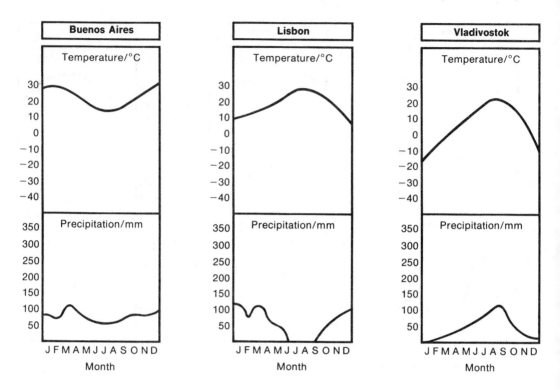

i) Which of the places is closest to the equator? Describe one feature of the climate which is typical of an equatorial region.

ii) Bahrain and Alice Springs are both in desert regions. Explain the difference in the shape of the temperature curves for the two places.

iii) Which two places (other than Bahrain and Alice Springs) have similar climates to each other?

iv) Which of the places has a monsoon season?

v) Which place is in a polar region? Describe its climate.

vi) Copy this table to compare the climates in Lisbon and Vladivostok and use information from the graphs to complete it.

	Lisbon	Vladivostok
Highest temperature recorded Month in which it was recorded		
Lowest temperature recorded Month in which it was recorded		
Highest rainfall recorded Month in which it was recorded		
Lowest rainfall recorded Month in which it was recorded		

5 Read the passage below. Use the information in the passage and your knowledge to answer the questions which follow.

> Over lengthy periods climate can change. A long-term shift of only 1 °C is enough to trigger such profound changes as the Little Ice Age in Western Europe, which peaked in the late 17th century. A drop of 4 °C is enough to bring on a full ice age. At the moment we are in one of the warmest phases of the past 1000 years. (In the northern hemisphere between 1881 and 1983, the warmest year was 1981.)
>
> Climatic change is the norm. The one thing that we can be sure about with regard to future climate is that it will feature deep-seated shifts, even if we leave it to get on with its own natural course – without disrupting it by, for example, contributing to carbon dioxide build-up in the atmosphere. This has major implications for our capacity to keep producing food. Throughout the world, climate is a critical factor in agriculture. During the late 1960s, the drought in the Sahel brought disaster to entire nations. In 1972 another drought inflicted such damage on the Soviet wheat crop that it helped to quadruple world prices within two years. In 1974, a delayed monsoon in India wrought havoc for millions of people. In 1975 pulses of cold air ravaged Brazil's coffee crop, causing inflationary upheavals in coffee prices around the world.
>
> Conversely, of course, a stable climate, or rather a climate with slow and predictable change, can be a tremendous asset that can basically enrich our lives.
>
> *Adapted from* Gaia Atlas of Planet Management.

a) Explain why 'climate is a critical factor in agriculture'.

b)   i) How are we 'contributing to carbon dioxide build-up in the atmosphere'?
     ii) What effect is this build-up likely to have on the Earth's climate?

c)   i) What happened to coffee prices in 1976?
     ii) Explain why this happened.

d) In recent years there have been droughts in Ethiopia and the Sudan. What was the effect on the people living in these areas?

e) What is meant by a 'stable climate'?

f) Why do you think the author describes a stable climate as 'a tremendous asset'?

6

Day: on-shore breeze   Night: off-shore breeze

The diagrams show the direction of coastal breezes by day and night.

a) Copy the diagrams.

b) Below are some statements about coastal breezes. Make a copy of the table below. Consider each pair of statements and decide which one goes into which column in the following table, then write in the statements.

During the day	During the night

i) Land (rocks, soil) warms up more quickly than water/Water cools down more slowly than land.

ii) Warmer air rises over the land/Warmer air rises over the sea.

iii) Colder air over the land is more dense and falls/Colder air over the sea is more dense and falls.

iv) Breezes blow from sea to land/Breezes blow from land to sea.

7

The diagram shows the movement of air between the Earth's surface and the tropopause in the northern hemisphere during April. Air rising above the equator can move in a northerly or southerly direction, returning to ground level about one-third of the way to the poles. Cold polar air descends and moves underneath warmer air from the equator. These general patterns persist throughout the year.

a) Describe how the height of the tropopause varies in the hemisphere.

b) What name is given to the transfer of heat by circulating currents like those around point A in the diagram?

    c) What causes air to rise above point X on the equator?

    d) Would you expect the air pressure at sea level near point X to be greater or less than that near point Y? Explain your answer.

    e) The wind patterns shown in the diagram, drift north or south on a seasonal basis. Suggest an explanation for this drift.

8 For each of the following changes, suggest one effect that the change would have on the surface conditions on Earth. Write out the completed table.

Change	*Effect of the change on surface conditions on Earth*
a) The average distance between the Sun and Earth decreases.	
b) The Sun's power output decreases.	
c) The Earth's rate of rotation decreases so that there are 265 days in one year.	
d) A series of volcanic eruptions fills the atmosphere with dust.	
e) The tilt of the Earth's axis increases from 23.5° to 28°.	

4.2 HUMAN INFLUENCES ON THE EARTH

4.2.1 The Local Environment

1

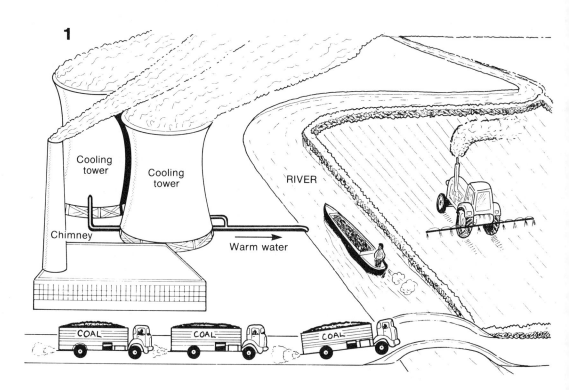

Look at the diagram and list all the examples of pollution you can see. Record your answer as shown below:

Name of pollutant	Where produced	One effect of this pollutant

2   In an attempt to get rid of a type of mosquito which was infesting a lake, the authorities sprayed the lake with the insecticide DDT. This appeared to be successful, since the mosquitoes died while other animals and plants seemed to be little affected. Consequently the treatment was repeated the next year. Some years later many large fish-eating birds were found to be dead or dying. When their bodies were analysed they were found to contain large amounts of DDT. Other animals and plants were examined and the results are shown in the table.

Organisms	Amount of DDT per unit mass
Small fish	10 units
Animal plankton	5 units
Plant plankton	1 unit
Large fish	100 units
Lake water	0.3 units
Grebes (fish-eating birds)	1600 units

a) Draw a food chain for the lake.

b) Why was such a high dosage of DDT found in grebes?

c) Why is DDT known as a persistent pesticide?

d) What steps can be taken to reduce pollution by pesticides?

3 Nitrogen is the most common gas in our atmosphere. Normally it is inert, but at high temperatures it can react with oxygen. A gas formed in this reaction, nitrogen monoxide, may lead to acid rain. Although nitrogen monoxide is neutral, it reacts instantly on contact with air to give the acidic gas nitrogen dioxide.

a) What does 'inert' mean?

b) Explain how nitrogen dioxide is produced by each of the following sources:

   i)   a coal-fired power station

   ii) a motor car

c) To reduce the pollution caused by nitrogen oxides, motor cars which run on unleaded petrol can be fitted with a catalytic converter. This uses a catalyst, and the high temperature in the exhaust pipe, to remove nitrogen monoxide by reacting it with another gas, carbon monoxide.

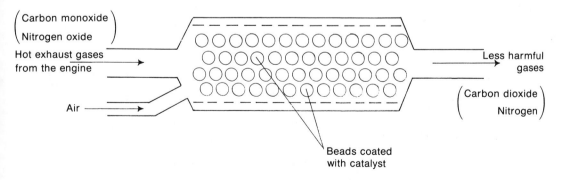

   i)   Explain how carbon monoxide is produced in a motor car engine.

   ii) What effect does carbon monoxide have on the human body?

   iii) What is a catalyst?

iv) Which of the two gases released from the converter does no harm to the environment? Explain your answer.

v) Suggest a reason for the fact that the catalytic converter can only be used on cars which run on unleaded petrol.

d) Coal-fired power stations can reduce the amount of nitrogen dioxide they produce by burning coal using 'fluidised bed' combustion. This allows the coal to burn efficiently at a lower temperature.

i) Explain how this method of burning coal reduces the amount of nitrogen dioxide emitted by the power station.

ii) Widespread use of fluidised bed technology would add around 5% to electricity bills. Explain, giving your reasons, whether you think that fluidised bed combustion should be introduced at all coal-fired power stations.

4 Cockshoot Broad is a lake in Norfolk. The map below shows that water flows into Cockshoot Broad from the River Bure. The area is surrounded by farmland that slopes down to the lake.

In recent years there has been a large increase in the levels of phosphate and nitrate in the waters of Cockshoot Broad.

a) Suggest where these chemicals could have come from.

b) When high levels of nitrate and phosphate pollute a lake or river, a series of changes takes place in the water, resulting in the death of many fish.

Rewrite the following sentences in the correct order to give a summary of the changes which occur.

Nitrates and phosphates provide essential minerals for the growth of microscopic algae.

Populations of bacteria increase and use up large amounts of oxygen.

Nitrates and phosphates pollute the water.

Oxygen levels in the water drop sharply.

The water becomes green and cloudy as the numbers of algae rise.

Fish die owing to lack of oxygen.

Many algae then die and provide food for decay bacteria.

c)   Why is there a build-up of dead organic matter on the bottom of polluted lakes and rivers?

d)   In some regions the level of nitrates in drinking water has increased. Why does this give cause for concern?

5 One way to check the amount of pollution in a river is to measure the volume of oxygen dissolved in the water. Another way is to see which sorts of animals are living in it.

This table shows the results of both methods. Use the information in the table to help you answer the questions which follow it.

Amount of pollution	Types of animal present		Volume of oxygen measured (cm^3/l of water)	
	Fish	Others	at 5°C	at 20°C
None	Grayling Salmon Trout	Mayfly nymph Stonefly nymph	8	5
Very little	Dace Roach	Freshwater shrimp Snail	6	4
Some	Gudgeon	Bloodworm Water louse	4	3
Lots	None	Rat-tailed maggot Sludge worm	2	1

a)   Which *two* animals would you expect to find in water with lots of pollution?

b)   Some fish farmers raise trout, which they set free in rivers for anglers to catch.

i)   Explain why these farmers need to be careful about the water supply they use on their fish farms.

ii)   What volume of oxygen, measured in centimetres cubed per litre, would you expect to find in a trout river at 20°C?

iii) Describe the pattern linking the temperature of the water and the amount of oxygen in it.

    iv) Suggest and explain what would happen to the number of trout if hot water from a factory was emptied into a trout river and increased the water temperature above 20 °C.

c) In 1974 salmon were caught in the River Thames for the first time in over a hundred years. What does this suggest about the water in the river before 1974?

4.2.2 Global Effects

1 The burning of fuels produces 14 000 million tonnes of carbon dioxide per year. Carbon dioxide is one of the gases in the atmosphere which allow short wavelength infra-red radiation from the Sun to pass through but which stop some of the long wavelength infra-red radiation from Earth leaving the atmosphere.

a) Why is the infra-red radiation re-emitted by the Earth of longer wavelength than that received?

b) The levels of carbon dioxide in the atmosphere are rising.

    i) What is the *main* human activity which is contributing to the increase?

    ii) Suggest and explain one other activity which may also be contributing to this increase.

c)   State and explain what effect the increase in CO_2 levels could have on the

    i)   climate in Britain

    ii)   mean sea level

d)   What effects might the changes you have described in c) have on the lives of people in Britain?

2   In April 1986, there was an explosion at the Chernobyl nuclear power station in Russia. Radioactivity escaped into the air and was later found to be in rain which fell on Europe.

The map below shows how quickly the radioactive rain spread across Europe.

Russia

Wales

Site of explosion
(April 26th)

KEY

✕————————✕ = Distance travelled
by radioactivity in one day

a)   How many days after the explosion did it take for the radioactive rain to reach Wales?

    The graph on page 30 shows the amount of radioactivity found in the meat of Welsh sheep in the days after the explosion.

b)   i)   How much radioactivity was found in the meat before the nuclear explosion?

    ii)   Suggest reasons for the presence of this radioactivity.

c)   i)   What was the highest level of radioactivity found in the meat?

    ii)   How many days after the explosion did it take to reach this level?

d)   When the radioactivity was found in the meat from sheep, the sale of this meat was stopped.

    How could radioactive meat harm human cells?

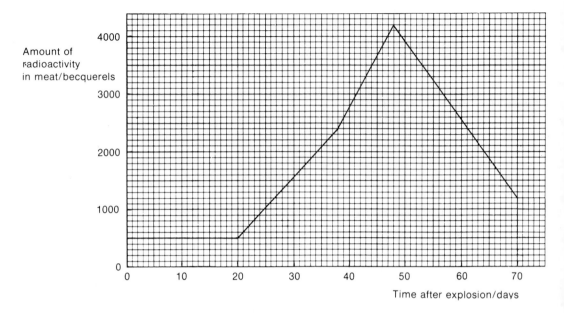

e) Use a table like the one below to list two advantages and two disadvantages of generating electricity using nuclear energy.

Advantages of nuclear energy	Disadvantages of nuclear energy

3 Read the passage below and answer the questions which follow.

Ozone is a form of oxygen which has three atoms per molecule. It occurs naturally in the upper atmosphere, where the ozone layer blocks most of the harmful ultraviolet radiation from the Sun. At ground level, ozone can be produced as a result of reactions between pollutants from car exhaust fumes and atmospheric gases. Low-level ozone is itself a pollutant, which can cause damage to trees and animals. It is a very reactive gas.

Recently, studies by scientists have shown that, while levels of ozone at ground level are increasing, the amount of ozone in the upper atmosphere is dropping. One factor which is thought to be partly responsible for this drop in ozone is the widespread use of chemicals called CFCs (chlorofluorocarbons). Following release into the atmosphere, CFCs break down and release chlorine, which reacts with ozone in the upper atmosphere.

In September 1987, the U.K. government signed the Montreal Protocol, agreeing to reduce the use of CFCs by 50% by the end of the century. Some scientists believe that this will not be enough to prevent large-scale damage to life on Earth.

a) What is the molecular formula of

i) 'normal' oxygen?

ii) ozone?

b) Give three common uses of CFCs.

c) Suggest one other source of atmospheric chlorine apart from CFCs.

d) Describe one possible consequence for humans of increased exposure to harmful ultraviolet radiation.

e) Suggest reasons why

   i)   levels of ozone at ground level are increasing

   ii) ozone produced at ground level does nothing to restore the ozone layer

f) How could *you* personally help to prevent the destruction of the ozone layer?

4   The diagram below supplies information about the sensitivity of some aquatic organisms to the pH of water.

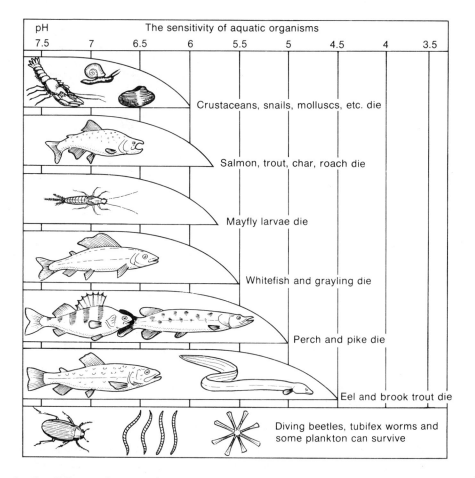

a) i)   What is the pH of water below which perch and pike cannot live?

   ii) Which organisms are tolerant of the most acid water?

b) Sulphur dioxide gas can react with other substances in the air producing an acid which lowers the pH of rain.

    i)   Name the acid which is formed.

    ii)   Name one other atmospheric pollutant which contributes to acid rain and say where it comes from.

This diagram shows a map of acid rain in western Europe.

KEY (pH of rain)

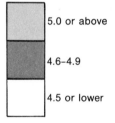

5.0 or above

4.6–4.9

4.5 or lower

c) Explain why the pH of the rain falling on Ireland is different from that falling on northern Europe.

d) In Sweden over 9000 lakes no longer contain live fish. Some of the lakes have become 100 times more acidic in the past 50 years.

Explain how this situation may have come about.

e) Most of the sulphur dioxide produced by coal-fired power stations could be removed by absorbing it using 'desulphurisation' equipment. Why is this *not* yet done on a large scale?

f) State *two* other ways in which this form of pollution could be reduced.

5   Write an article for a newspaper which discusses the issues surrounding the destruction of rainforests. You may use the information below to help you.

Rainforests are being destroyed by Man to provide timber and to clear land for ranching and farming, mining and new roads.

About half of the world's rainforest has already gone. An area the size of England, Scotland and Wales goes up in smoke every year.

Tropical hardwoods and the cash crops grown on cleared land provide important income for some poor, developing countries.

Large areas of rainforest in Central America have been cut down to provide grazing for cattle for the American hamburger market. Alternatively it is cleared to grow crops such as soya beans to feed European cattle.

About 200 million tribal people live in the rainforests of the world.

Tropical rainforests soak up water like giant sponges. If trees are cut down in large numbers, the rainwater floods the land. Transpiration from the leaves of the plants is an important part of the water cycle.

Once the trees have gone the rainforest soil will only support the growth of crops or provide grazing for a few years.

A typical patch of rainforest, just 4 miles square, contains as many as 1500 species of flowering plants, up to 750 species of tree, 400 species of bird, 150 kinds of butterfly, 100 different types of reptile and 60 species of amphibian. The numbers of insects are so great that no one has yet been able to count them.

In 1960 four out of every five children who got leukaemia died. Now four out of every five survive thanks to a drug derived from the rosy periwinkle which grows in the rainforests of Madagascar.

4.2.3 Recycling Waste

1

Mr Jolly has a compost bin in his garden. It is made of a steel frame which is coated in plastic. Plastic panels fit into the sides and bottom of the frame. The plastic panels on the sides have holes in them.

a) Suggest one reason why

    i)   the frame is made of steel

    ii)   the panels are made of plastic

    iii) the steel frame is coated in plastic

Mr Jolly puts all of his vegetable waste in the compost bin. When the bin is full the waste is left for 12 months. Mr Jolly sometimes waters the compost heap during the summer. After 12 months the vegetable waste has been converted to compost.

b) Why does Mr Jolly only put vegetable waste in the compost bin and not all of his household waste such as plastic bags, glass bottles and metal cans?

c) Bacteria break down the vegetable waste into compost. Where do the bacteria come from?

d) How do these decay bacteria contribute to

    i)   the carbon cycle?

    ii)   the nitrogen cycle?

e) Why does Mr Jolly need to water the compost bin sometimes during the summer?

f) Sometimes small bits of waste fall out through the holes in the sides of the compost bin. Explain why it would *not* be a good idea for Mr Jolly to block the holes up.

g) Why doesn't Mr Jolly put the vegetable waste straight on to his garden instead of first converting it into compost?

h) i) Much of the refuse collected from houses is buried in the ground. Suggest TWO ways in which this refuse could be put to better use and explain the advantages of your suggestions. Organise your answer in the form of a table:

Use	Advantage

ii) Explain how, in some places, refuse buried in the ground years ago is now providing a useful fuel.

2 a) Why should people be discouraged from using plastic packaging?

b) A supermarket claims that its carrier bags are biodegradable.

Design an experiment to test whether their claim is correct.

3 Carefully read the passage below which is about recycling paper, and answer the questions which follow.

At the moment, about 40% of the trees which are cut down are used for making wood pulp, which is then made into paper. Only 25% of the world's paper is currently recycled, although there is no good technical or economic reason why this recycling rate could not be doubled in the next ten years. Recycling half of the world's paper consumption would meet almost 75% of new paper demand and would prevent millions of hectares of forest from being damaged. Fibre-rich countries like Canada and Sweden are not in the front rank of paper recyclers. Recycling rates are much higher in such fibre-poor countries as Japan, Mexico and the Netherlands. In order to recycle, the waste paper needs to be collected and sorted. Most of the best quality paper for recycling comes from the printing industry and offices. Household waste paper is of a lower quality being mainly newspapers which have a lot of ink on them. The ink must first be removed from the waste paper if high quality recycled paper is to be produced. This is done with caustic soda and hot water. Only about 5–6% is treated in this way because it is quite an expensive process. The remainder is simply pulped with hot water, then screened and washed to remove dirt. Paper recycled in this way is only good enough for making such things as cardboard and paper towels.

a) Why does recycling paper help to conserve forests?

b) Canada and Sweden are described as 'fibre-rich'. What does this mean?

c) Why do you think 'fibre-poor' countries recycle more paper?

d) Where does the best quality paper for recycling come from?

e) i)   How is waste paper treated to remove ink?

    ii) Why is only a small percentage of paper to be recycled treated in this way?

e) Suggest ways in which people could be encouraged to save waste for recycling.

4   Look carefully at the diagram below which shows part of the water cycle in nature, and answer the questions which follow.

a) What is happening at A and B on the diagram?

b) Where is the purest water to be found?

c) Explain how smoke from the factory (G) could affect life in the lake (F).

d) i)   If the farmer puts too much fertiliser on his fields at area C, what will happen to the excess?

    ii) How will this affect the plant life in the sea?

e) How could the cutting down of large areas of forest such as E affect the water cycle?

f) Explain how this deforestation could also lead to

   i)   soil erosion

   ii) flooding

   iii) silting up of the river

g) Explain how it is possible that one of the residents at D has used some of the water which the farmer drank a year ago.

4.3 THE EARTH IN SPACE

4.3.1 The Solar System

1   The following diagram shows part of the **solar system** (not to scale).

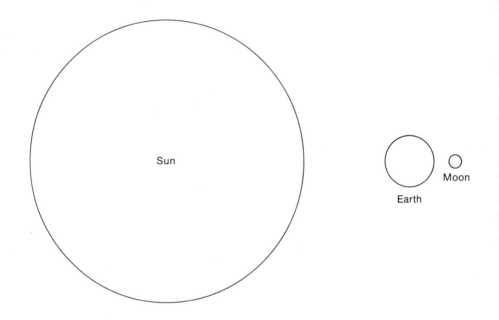

a)   Which of the bodies is a **star**?

b)   Why is the Moon not a **planet**?

c)   Name two planets which orbit closer to the Sun than the Earth does.

d)   When Columbus set sail to find the New World in 1492, people thought he would fall off the edge of the Earth. What evidence do we have that the Earth is not flat?

2   Pair these groups of words to form correct statements.

We experience day and night on Earth once every 24 hours because   the Earth's axis is tilted at $23\frac{1}{2}°$.

We see different phases of the Moon in a regular cycle because   the Earth completes one orbit of the Sun in one year.

There are seasonal changes in climate on Earth because	the Earth rotates once on its axis once in one day.
We see different constellations (star patterns) at different times of year because	the Moon rotates once on its axis in the same time that it takes to complete one orbit of the Earth.
We only ever see about one half of the Moon's surface from Earth because	the Moon orbits the Earth approximately once every 28 days.

3   The diagram below shows the Moon orbiting the Earth. Four positions in the orbit are shown.

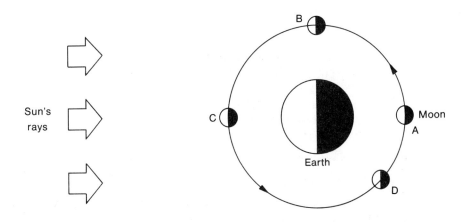

a)   The Moon has no light of its own. Explain why we can see the Moon shining in the sky.

b)   Draw and name the phases of the moon as they would be seen from a point on Earth when the Moon is at

i) position A

ii) position B

iii) position D

c)   At what position must the Moon be for a total eclipse of the Sun to occur?

d)   Explain why a total eclipse of the Moon is not seen every time the Moon passes through position A.

4   Read the passage below which is about **tides**. Answer the questions which follow.

> Much of the Earth's surface is covered with water. Because water is a fluid it can move easily in response to gravity. The gravitational pull of the Moon causes the waters to rise and fall, in most places twice very 24 hours 50 minutes. When a particular part of the Earth is in line with the Moon, the water bulges and the tide rises. As the Earth spins on its axis the bulge moves across the oceans like a giant wave. The diagram below assumes that all the Earth is covered with water to make it easier to interpret.

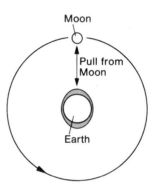

> The Sun has a similar but smaller gravitational effect. At New Moon and Full Moon both Sun and Moon are in line with the Earth. The combined effect means that the tides are at their highest and are called **spring** tides. At First and Last Quarter Moon the Sun and Moon are at right angles. The gravitational pull of the Moon is partly cancelled out by the gravitational pull of the Sun. The tides are at their lowest and are called **neap** tides.

a)   What is responsible for creating the rise and fall of the tides?

b)   How often is there a high tide in most places on Earth?

c)   Approximately how much of the Earth's surface is actually covered with water? (You may need to use a reference book.)

d)   Explain the difference between spring and neap tides.

e)   Draw diagrams which show the relative positions of the Earth, oceans, Moon and Sun at

  i) spring tide at New Moon.

  ii) neap tide at First Quarter.

5   The diagram opposite, which is not drawn to scale, shows the Sun–Earth arrangement during summer and winter.

a)   Which feature shown in the diagram is responsible for the seasonal changes in climate experienced on Earth?

b)   By referring to the diagram, explain how the northern hemisphere experiences summer while the southern hemisphere experiences winter.

c) At midsummer in the northern hemisphere, what is the minimum latitude from which you would be able to see the Sun above the horizon for 24 hours each day?

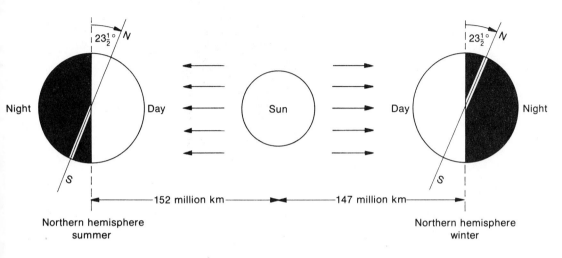

Northern hemisphere
summer

Northern hemisphere
winter

6 The diagram below, which is not to scale, shows how an eclipse of the Sun occurs when the shadow of the Moon falls on the Earth.

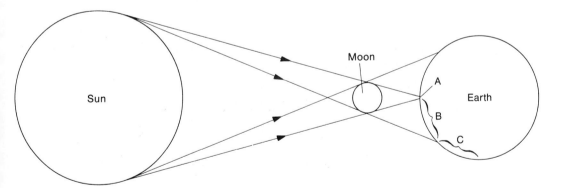

a) Copy the diagram.

b) Describe what you would see from the Earth during a total eclipse of the Sun.

c) From which of the regions A, B or C on Earth would an observer see
   i) a total eclipse of the Sun?
   ii) a partial eclipse of the Sun?

d) i) Draw a second diagram showing the Moon in a position where a suitably placed astronaut on the Moon would see a total eclipse of the Sun.

   ii) What would an observer on the night side of the Earth see when the Moon is in this position?

7

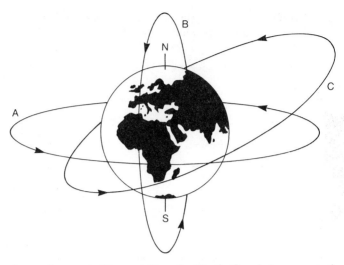

The diagram shows three satellites orbiting the Earth. One is in a geostationary orbit.

a)   Which satellite is in a polar orbit?

b)   i) Explain what is meant by a 'geostationary' orbit.

ii) Which satellite is in a geostationary orbit?

c)   What force holds the satellites in orbit?

d)   Write down *three* different uses of satellites. In each case say how they have improved our way of life.

8   The following table gives the average density of the planets, listed in alphabetical order. The value for Pluto has been left out.

Planet	Density (kg/m³)
Earth	5500
Jupiter	1300
Mars	4000
Mercury	5400
Neptune	1700
Pluto	
Saturn	700
Uranus	1300
Venus	5200

a)   Arrange the planets in order of increasing distance from the Sun using a reference book if necessary.

b)   Construct a bar graph showing the density of the planets placed in order of increasing distance from the Sun.

c)   What is the overall pattern in the density of the planets in the solar system?

d)   Use your bar graph to estimate the density of Pluto. What assumption do you have to make in estimating this value?

e) The solar system can be divided into two groups of planets, the *terrestrial planets,* which have densities similar to the Earth, and the *gas giants,* which have densities close to that of water ($1000 \, kg/m^3$). Which planets would you place in each group? Give your answer in the form of a table.

f) One theory concerning the early history of the solar system states that the high temperatures close to the Sun caused volatile, low density materials to 'boil away'. These materials then 'condensed' further out from the Sun.

i) Does this theory account for the pattern in density of the planets?

ii) In addition to temperature, what other factor must be considered in deciding whether the gases in a planet's atmosphere can escape into space?

g) Name one other type of object in the solar system apart from the Sun and planets.

9 The formula for the force of attraction between two masses, m and M, with centres separated by a distance d, is

$$\text{force} = \frac{GMm}{d^2} \quad (G \text{ is the gravitational constant})$$

Use this formula to predict:

a) the change in the force of attraction between two objects when the mass of one of them is doubled.

b) the change in the force of attraction when the distance between the masses is doubled.

c) the change in the force of attraction between the Earth and the Sun if the Sun collapsed to become a black hole without loss of mass.

4.3.2 Stars and Galaxies

1 a) What is the difference between a planet and a star?

b) Explain why the apparent motion of planets in the sky is visible from night to night, yet the stars keep their positions for centuries.

c) Give one reason, not concerned with motion, why the appearance of the night sky will be different in several million years' time.

2

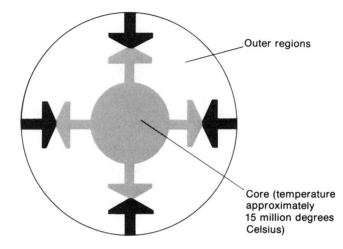

Outer regions

Core (temperature
approximately
15 million degrees
Celsius)

The diagram shows the balance of forces in a star such as the Sun. Outward pressure from nuclear reactions in the core balances the inward pressure from the weight of the outer regions. This balance may remain for between one million and a million million years, depending on the mass of the star. The nuclear reactions in the core occur at a greater rate as the temperature increases, and produce heavier elements (such as helium and carbon) from hydrogen. When the core hydrogen is used up, the period of stability comes to an end.

a) What *type* of nuclear reaction takes place in the star's core?

b) What is the force which pulls the outer regions of the star towards the centre?

c) Which chemical element is the most common in stars like the Sun?

d) What would happen to the outward pressure from the core if the temperature there increased?

e) A more massive star must support the greater inward pressure from heavier outer layers. Would you expect the temperature at the core to be greater or less than that in the Sun? Explain your choice.

f) Use the diagram to predict what happens to a star when nuclear reactions in the core stop.

g) It is thought that the Sun can maintain this balance for around ten thousand million years. Give one piece of evidence from the passage which suggests that a more massive 'giant' star will become out of balance sooner.

3 a) What is the difference between a **constellation** and a **star cluster**?

b) The diagrams opposite show how the star pattern in the constellation Cassiopeia will change with time:

| 1989 | 26 989 | 51 989 |

    i) What is the cause of the changing pattern?

    ii) Why does it appear to change so slowly?

c)   When we measure the velocities of distant galaxies by analysing light from them, they all appear to be moving away from us.

    i) What is the cause of this motion?

    ii) Using the diagram of a model universe below, explain why our Milky Way galaxy is not the centre of the universe in spite of the observation that galaxies are moving away in all directions.
(Hint: view the change from any other galaxy.)

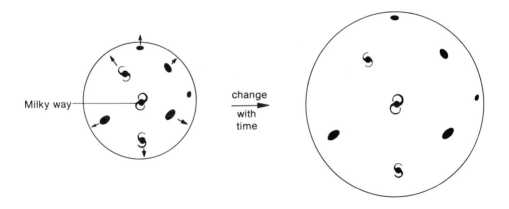

d)   What force may ultimately halt the expansion of the universe?

4 a)   What is the difference between astronomy and astrology?

  b)   Describe how you would set up a test to investigate the accuracy of astrological predictions in horoscopes. Assume that you have a set of horoscopes for the last week, taken from some magazines, and that there is at least one person from each zodiac 'birth sign' in your class. Write your answer as a sequence of steps, making sure that you consider the following points:

      Include enough detail to allow somebody else to use your method after reading it.

How would you ensure that the test was fair?

How would you decide whether the predictions were accurate on the basis of your test?

c)   What problems are there with scientific testing of subjects like astrology, regardless of how fair the test is?

TOPIC 5

Forces and Energy

5.1   Forces
5.1.1   Pushes and Pulls
5.1.2   Turning Forces
5.1.3   Pressure
5.1.4   Moving Objects
5.1.5   Mass and Momentum
5.1.6   Structures and Materials

5.2   Energy
5.2.1   Fuels and Energy Resources
5.2.2   Waves
5.2.3   Energy Transfer

5.3   Sound and Music
5.3.1   Sound and Hearing
5.3.2   Audio Devices
5.3.3   Vibrations and Musical Instruments
5.3.4   Using Sound

5.4   Electricity and Magnetism
5.4.1   Static Electricity
5.4.2   Circuits
5.4.3   Electricity in Use
5.4.4   Magnetism
5.4.5   Electromagnetic Effects
5.4.6   Cathode Rays

5.5   Using Light and Electromagnetic Radiation
5.5.1   Shadows and Illusions
5.5.2   Refraction and Lenses
5.5.3   The Eye
5.5.4   Optical Devices
5.5.5   Electromagnetic Radiation

5.1 FORCES

5.1.1 Pushes and Pulls

1 a) Choose all the words from the list below which could correctly complete this sentence:

Forces can change the _____ of an object.

colour   direction of movement   mass   shape   size   speed

b) Copy and complete this statement of Newton's first law of motion:

A body stays at _____ or moves at a constant _____ in a _____ line unless it is acted upon by an external _____.

c) Copy and complete these sentences:

Forces are measured in units called _____.

The pull of the Earth or the force of gravity on a body is called its _____ and is measured in _____.

The pull of the Earth on a mass of 1 kg is approximately _____.

d) Which force is responsible for the following effects?
   i) A book sliding across a desk slows down and stops.
   ii) A book falls to the ground when dropped.
   iii) The Moon remains in orbit around the Earth.
   iv) A polystyrene block rises to the water's surface when released from the bottom of a swimming pool.

2 a) i) List *four* ways in which friction is a nuisance.
          ii) List *four* ways in which friction is useful.

b) Explain
   i) how aborigines can light fires by rubbing two sticks together.
   ii) why spacecraft can get very hot when they re-enter the Earth's atmosphere.

c) i) What single word would describe the *shape* of a rocket, a high speed train, a fish, and a cheetah at full speed?
   ii) What is the advantage of being such a shape?

d) List *five* ways of reducing friction.

e) You are walking to school one day and the force of friction suddenly disappears.
    Write an account of what might happen.

3 Here is a hypothesis:

> The static friction force between an object (such as a wooden block) and the
> floor is independent of the surface area of the object which is in contact with
> the floor.

Design an experiment to test this hypothesis.

4 Copy and complete these sentences about balanced and unbalanced forces,
choosing words from this list to fill in the blanks.

> **acceleration   balanced   constant   equilibrium   unbalanced**

a) If the forces acting on a body are _____, the body will be stationary or
    move at a _____ speed in a straight line.

b) If the forces acting on a body are _____, the body will accelerate.

c) A body is said to be in _____ under the action of several forces when it
    has an _____ of zero.

5 The following objects are in equilibrium. Copy (or trace) each diagram and draw in
the missing force or forces, paying particular attention to their direction of action.
Label all the forces, choosing your answer from the following list. (Each one may be
used more than once if necessary.)

> **reaction   weight   tension   drag   friction**

a)

A girl stationary on a swing. Force shown: **weight**

b)

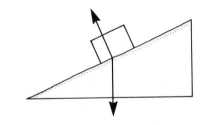

An aircraft flying straight and level at constant speed. Forces shown: **thrust** and **lift**.

c)

A block resting on a rough, inclined surface. Forces shown: **weight** and **reaction**.

d)

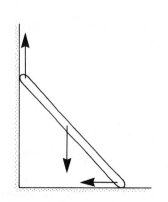

A rod resting at an angle against a wall. Forces shown: **weight** and **friction**.

6 When a 20 g mass is suspended from a spring, the extension produced in the spring is 10 cm.

Total load 20 g

10 cm

What extension would you expect in each of the identical springs, in the following experiments?

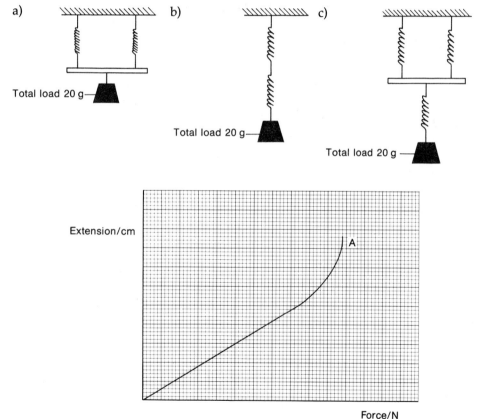

a) Total load 20 g

b) Total load 20 g

c) Total load 20 g

7

Extension/cm

A

Force/N

The graph shows how the extension produced in a spring varies as the force applied to the spring increases.

a) State Hooke's law. When does it apply?

b) Copy the graph and label the following:

   i) the elastic limit

   ii) the region where Hooke's law is obeyed

c) i) Label a point X on the curve where plastic deformation has occurred.

   ii) What would you see happening to the spring if the magnitude of the applied force was increased beyond point A?

8 a) Copy and complete the sentences below using the words **size** or **direction** to fill in the blanks.

   i) Force is a vector quantity because both _____ and _____ are important.

   ii) Scalar quantities have only _____ and no _____ .

b) Give *two* other examples of vector quantities.

c) Give *three* examples of scalar quantities.

9 The diagrams below show the size and direction of a number of forces applied to a wooden block. Draw a similar diagram for each example, which shows the magnitude (size) and direction of the single resultant (overall) force. Show how you arrived at your answer for parts c) to f).

10

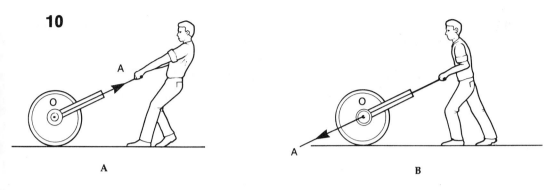

a) The diagram A shows a man pulling a garden roller with a force represented by the line OA. On a similar diagram (you need not draw the man), show the horizontal and the vertical components of the force.

b) The diagram B shows a man pushing a garden roller with a force represented by the line OA. On a similar diagram show the horizontal and vertical components of the force.

c) The man wants to move his garden roller to a different part of his garden across a wet muddy lawn. Should he pull or push the roller? Explain your answer.

d) On another occasion he wants to roll his dry lawn. Should he pull or push this time? Explain your answer.

e) The diagram below shows a barge being towed from the canal bank. To avoid hitting the bank, the barge must steer towards the centre of the river. Copy the diagram and draw in the forces acting, to explain why this is so.

11   A weight of 12 N is suspended by a rope. A horizontal force of 5 N is then applied as shown in the diagram. Find the tension T in the rope.

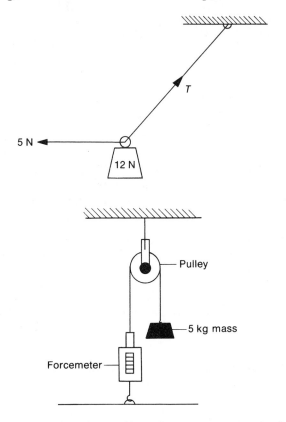

12

A 5 kg mass is suspended over a pulley. The rope is connected to a forcemeter which has its hook anchored to the floor. What is the reading on the forcemeter? ($g = 10$ N/kg)

13   a)   State Newton's third law of motion.

   b)   Two students are pulling against each other using force metres attached to the ends of a length of rope.

   If force meter A reads 60 N, what will B read?

   c)   Explain why a fireman must brace himself as he aims a fire hose. Write an equation for the action and reaction involved.

5.1.2 Turning Forces

1   When Margaret and Richard sit on the see-saw it does not balance:

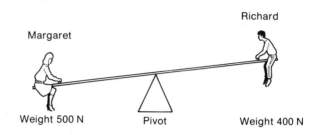

Richard

Margaret

Weight 500 N   Pivot   Weight 400 N

   a)   What force is needed on Richard's end of the see-saw to balance it? Give the direction and size of the force.

   b)   Who must move closer to the pivot to balance the see-saw?

2   Describe how you would use the following apparatus to find the mass of a potato, estimated to be 200 g.

     metre rule balanced on a nail through its mid-point

     string, as required

     one 150 g mass, with a hole at its centre

     one potato

3 The **moment** of a force about a pivot is given by the expression

moment = magnitude of force × perpendicular distance from pivot

A moment has a turning effect on objects.

a) i) Why is it very difficult to close a door by pushing close to the hinges, yet very easy when the same force is applied near the handle?

ii) Why is it easier to rotate a nut using a spanner with a long handle?

b) Where should a downward force of 200 N be applied to balance the beam shown below?

4 The bottle in the diagram is in equilibrium in three positions A, B and C.

a) In which position is the bottle in
    i) stable equilibrium?
    ii) unstable equilibrium?
    iii) neutral equilibrium?
    Explain your choices.

b) Copy this sentence choosing only the correct alternative from inside the brackets.

To be more stable an object should have a (high/low) centre of mass and a (narrow/broad) base.

c) Why does the giraffe shown here splay out its front legs as it takes a drink?

5 The object drawn below has the centre of mass marked by a small circle. Describe the effect of the force or forces acting on the object in each situation. All forces shown have the same magnitude.

a)

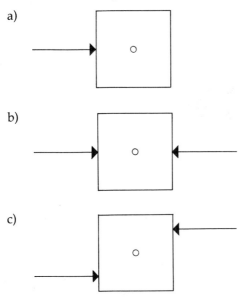

b)

c)

6 A 'manoeuvring unit' (MU) designed to allow astronauts to travel from the Space Shuttle on short journeys into space is shown in the diagram. It is fitted with a compressed gas cylinder and six jets which can fire jets of gas in the directions indicated. By activating certain jets the astronaut is able to move in any desired direction. The force exerted by each jet acts through the centre of mass of the astronaut-chair unit, and the jets are arranged in opposing pairs.

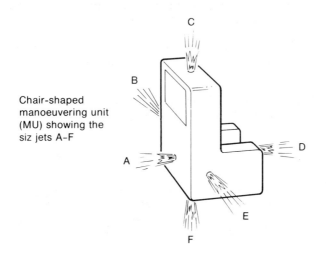

Chair-shaped manoeuvering unit (MU) showing the siz jets A–F

Chair-shaped manoeuvring unit (MU) showing the six jets A–F.

On one particular mission to repair a damaged satellite (mass 11 000 kg) in orbit an astronaut emerges from the Shuttle and moves towards the satellite along the route indicated. (The diagram is not to scale.)

a) To move off as shown, the astronaut fires a short burst of gas from jet C. Write down the complete sequence of jets which must be fired to enable the astronaut to follow the route indicated. Assume that each jet exerts the same force for the same time.

b) What advantage is there in arranging the jets of the MU

   i) in opposing pairs?

   ii) so that all exert a force through the centre of mass of the system?

c) The journey to the satellite takes 1 minute and 20 seconds. Calculate the average speed of the astronaut in m/s. (Formula: distance = speed × time.)

d) Is it possible for the astronaut to make the MU rotate while strapped in and well away from other objects? Explain your answer.

e) While trying to turn a screw on one of the satellite panels, the astronaut and MU begin to rotate. Explain how this occurs.

7 Study the diagrams of the three classes of lever shown below, then decide to which class each of the levers a)–f) belongs.

a)
b)
c)
d)
e)
f)

5.1.3 Pressure

1 Copy and complete this formula:

$$\text{force} = \underline{\hspace{3cm}} \times \text{area}$$
$$(N) \qquad\qquad (m^2)$$

(You may need to use this formula in the questions which follow.)

2 A rectangular block has dimensions $10 \times 20 \times 40$ cm. It is made from material with density 2200 kg/m^3.

a) What is the volume of the block in m^3?

b) What is the mass of the block?

c) What is the weight of the block? ($g = 10$ N/kg)

d) What pressure does the block exert when standing on its smallest face?

e) Would the block float or sink in water (density 1000 kg/m^3)? Explain your answer.

(Additional formula: mass = volume × density.)

3 Calculate the pressure in Pa (1 Pa = 1 N/m²) exerted in the following situations:

a) a circus stilt-walker, total weight 1000 N, balancing on one stilt (area 0.001 m²).

b) a circus elephant, weight 50 000 N, balancing on its hind legs (total surface area in contact with the ground 0.10 m²).

4 A hydraulic jack is shown below.

Effort 800 N

Load

Area 0.1 m²

Area 0.4 m²

a) What pressure does the effort exert?

b) What force is transmitted to the load?

c) What is the mechanical advantage of the jack?

$$\left(\text{Additional formula: mechanical advantage} = \frac{\text{load}}{\text{effort}}. \right)$$

5

Fulcrum

Load

Safety valve

STEAM BOILER

The diagram shows a steam boiler safety valve, which is designed to operate when the pressure in the boiler reaches 200 kPa.

a) Write down the pressure, in N/m^2, at which the valve operates.

b) In the arrangement shown, the downward force on the valve due to the load is 500 N. Calculate the area of the hole in which the valve is seated.

c) Would the valve operating pressure increase or decrease if the load was moved closer to the fulcrum? Explain your choice.

6 A length of rubber tubing is filled with water and lowered into a water tank as shown in the diagram.

X

A →

Water tank —

← E

← D

Water-filled rubber tubing

B   C

Z

Bung

a) At which two of the positions A–E is the pressure on the inside wall of the tank the same?

b) i) What is the pressure inside the tubing at X?

 ii) Is the pressure at Z greater or less than that of X? Explain your answer.

c) Describe fully what happens when the bung at Z is removed. Give reasons for your answer.

5.1.4 Moving Objects

1   Prakesh decides to go to Amrit's home to collect some heavy books. The graph
shows how his distance from home (in metres) changes with time (in minutes):

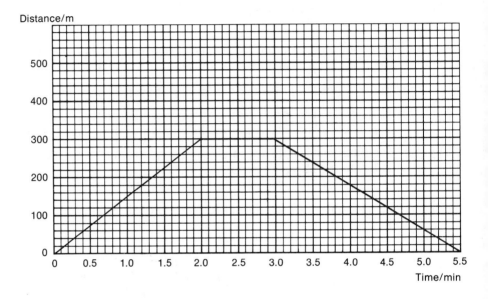

a)   How long did it take Prakesh to reach Amrit's home?

b)   How far away is Amrit's house?

c)   What was Prakesh's average speed on the outward journey in m/s?

d)   How long did Prakesh stay at Amrit's house?

2 a)   Copy and complete this formula.

$$\text{average speed} = \frac{\underline{\hspace{2cm}}\text{ travelled}}{\underline{\hspace{2cm}}\text{ taken}}$$

b)   Calculate the average speed of the following:
   i)   a runner who travels 100 m in 10 s
   ii) a cyclist who travels 48 km in 3 hours
   iii) a car which travels 240 km in 3 hours
   iv) a rocket which travels 400 000 km in 80 hours

3 Copy and complete the passage below which is about speed and velocity. Choose words from this list to fill in the blanks:

> constant   direction   gradient   scalar   speed   straight
> time   vector

The velocity of an object is an indication of both the speed and the _____ in which it is moving. Velocity is a _____ quantity, whilst speed is a _____ quantity. Plotting a graph of the distance travelled against _____ taken allows us to find the _____ of an object. If the body is travelling at a _____ speed the graph will be a _____ line and the speed will be the _____ of that line.

4 A student set up the following experiment to measure the velocity of a trolley moving down a slope.

The card on the trolley blocks the light from the bulb as the trolley moves down the runway. The time taken for the card to pass in front of the photocell is recorded on the timer.

a) i) If the trolley moves down the runway at constant velocity, what can you say about the forces acting on the trolley while it is moving?

   ii) What information, other than the reading on the timer, is needed to calculate the velocity of the trolley?

b) The angle of the slope is increased so that the trolley accelerates down the runway.

   i) What forces are acting on the trolley in the direction of the slope? Comment on the relative size of these forces.

   ii) Describe how you would modify the experiment in order to calculate the acceleration of the trolley. List any additional measurements you would need to take, and how you would calculate the acceleration of the trolley from your measurements.

5 a) Copy and complete the formula

distance travelled = _____ × time taken

b) The nearest star to the Sun (and Earth), Proxima Centauri, is approximately 4 light years from Earth. 1 light year may be taken to be 9 million million km $(9 \times 10^{12}$ km). How long would it take a space ship, travelling at 60 000 kilometres per hour, to reach Proxima Centauri?

6 Acceleration is given by the formula

$$acceleration = \frac{change\ in\ velocity\ (m/s)}{time\ taken\ for\ change\ (s)}$$

Copy the formula and add the units used to measure acceleration.

7 A new sports car undergoing trials accelerates to 30 m/s. After maintaining this speed for some time it decelerates to rest in two stages. This information is shown on the velocity–time graph.

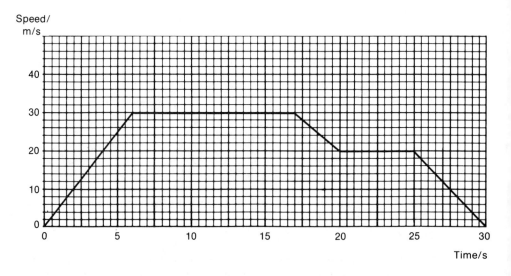

a) What was the acceleration of the car during the first six seconds?

b) i) For what length of time was the car travelling at 30 m/s?
    ii) What distance did it travel in that time?

c) Find the total distance travelled during the short trial by calculating the area under the graph.

d) Copy and complete the following:

If a graph is plotted of speed against time an object's _____ can be found by the _____ of the graph. The area under the graph gives the total _____ travelled.

8 Calculate the acceleration of the following objects, stating the units clearly.

a) A sprinter accelerating from rest to a velocity of 5 m/s in 5 s.

b) A falling apple which hits the ground at 5 m/s after falling for 0.5 s.

c) A rocket which reaches a velocity of 150 km/h, 5 s after launch.

d) A train which decelerates uniformly from 120 km/h and stops after 1 min.

e) A car which crashes at 50 km/h and is brought to rest in 1 s.

(Formula: change in velocity = acceleration × time taken.)

9 a) Copy and complete this formula. Include units inside the brackets.

force (_____) = _____ (_____) × acceleration (_____)

b) Use the formula to calculate the acceleration of a lorry, mass 3000 kg, when acted on by a force of 2400 N.

c) What force is needed to decelerate the same lorry at 2.0 m/s²?

d) A second lorry accelerates at 0.5 m/s² when acted on by a force of 2200 N. What is its mass?

10 A car of mass 1200 kg, is travelling at a steady 30 m/s. The driver brakes and the car stops after 6 s.

a) Assuming that the deceleration is uniform, how fast is the car travelling 3 s after the brakes are applied?

b) Calculate the deceleration in m/s².

c) What braking force was applied?
(Formulae: change in velocity = acceleration × time taken
force = mass × acceleration.)

11 Rotary motion can be transferred using meshed gear wheels. In the example drawn below, the driver wheel (input) has 20 teeth, and the driven wheel (output) has 10 teeth.

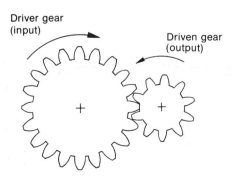

Driver gear (input)

Driven gear (output)

a) When the driver gear has completed one revolution, how many revolutions has the driven gear completed?

b) To enable the output rotation to be in the same direction as that of the input, a third 'idler' gear can be introduced between the two gear wheels.

   i) Draw a diagram to show how this is achieved.

   ii) Would the number of teeth on the idler gear make any difference to the relative rate of rotation of the input and output gear wheels?

12 a) Copy and complete this sentence.

To maintain circular motion, a force acting towards the _____ of the circle is needed, which is known as the centripetal force.

b) In each of the following situations, an object is in circular motion. Identify the centripetal force in each case.

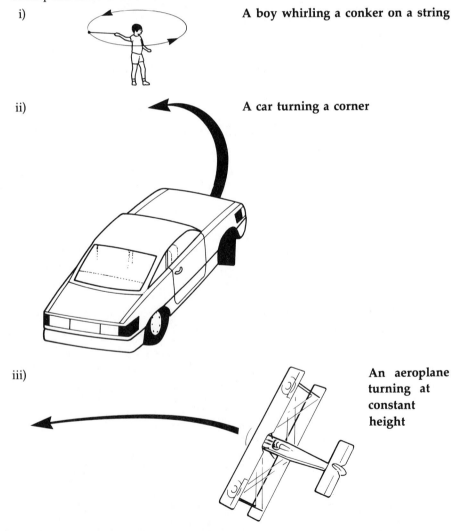

i) **A boy whirling a conker on a string**

ii) **A car turning a corner**

iii) **An aeroplane turning at constant height**

iv) 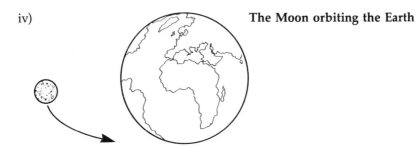 **The Moon orbiting the Earth**

13 Below are some pairs of statements about kinetic and potential energy. Consider each pair and decide which one to put into which column in a table with the headings shown below. Copy and complete the table.

Gravitational potential energy	*Kinetic energy*

a) Energy that a body has because of its movement.
Energy that a body has because of its position.

b) A diver standing on the high board has it.
A fast moving racing car on a level track has it.

c) It increases as an object accelerates (horizontally).
It increases as an object is raised to a greater height (at a steady rate).

d) It is found using the formula: mass × g × height
(kg)　(10 N/kg)　(m)
It is found using the formula: 1/2 × mass × velocity squared
(kg)　　　$(m/s)^2$

e) Is measured in joules.
Is also measured in joules.

14 The kinetic energy of an object of mass m (kg) moving with velocity v (m/s) is given by the formula

$$\text{kinetic energy} = \tfrac{1}{2}mv^2$$

Use this expression to calculate the kinetic energy (J) of the following objects.

a) A snowball, mass 0.1 kg, thrown at 12 m/s.

b) An athlete, mass 50 kg, running at a steady 8 m/s.

c) A bullet, mass 20 g, travelling at 500 m/s.

d) A proton, mass 1.7×10^{-27} kg travelling at 3.0×10^7 m/s.

e) An insect, mass 1.5 g, crawling at 0.02 m/s.

15 A pendulum bob is originally at rest at O, suspended from point X. It is raised to point A then released. It travels past O and reaches point C. Copy the diagram together with the following sentences, which you should complete by adding the appropriate word or words.

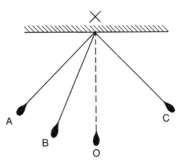

a) At point A, the pendulum bob has _____ energy only.

b) At point B the pendulum bob has both _____ and _____ energy.

c) At point O, after being released, the pendulum bob has _____ energy only.

d) The velocity of the bob is greatest at point _____.

e) The acceleration of the bob is greatest at points _____ and _____.

16 The overall stopping distances for a car travelling at various speeds are listed in the table.

Car speed (m.p.h.)	Thinking distance (feet)	Braking distance (feet)	Overall stopping distance (feet)
30	30	45	75
40	40	80	120
50	50	125	175
60	60	180	240
70	70	245	315

a) i) What is the 'thinking distance'?

ii) Using the pattern in the thinking distances, write down the thinking distance in feet when travelling at 100 m.p.h.

b) i) What is the pattern relating the braking distance (in feet) to the speed of the car (in m.p.h.)?

ii) Use your answer to b) i) to calculate the braking distance for a car travelling at 100 m.p.h.

c) What is the overall stopping distance for a car travelling at 100 m.p.h.?

d) List three reasons why the actual stopping distance for a car travelling at 100 m.p.h. may not be the same as the value correctly calculated in part c).

17 a) Copy and complete the following sentence by choosing the correct alternative inside each bracket.

The greater the (force/speed/time) of an object, the greater the (force/speed/time) needed to stop it in a given (force/speed/time).

b) Study the table below, which gives the minimum stopping distance for a locomotive travelling at various speeds.

Speed (m/s)	Stopping distance (m)
10	40
20	160
30	360
40	640

i) Plot a graph of stopping distance against speed and use it to estimate the stopping distance when the locomotive is travelling at 25 m/s.

ii) Assuming that the locomotive decelerates uniformly, calculate the time taken to stop when travelling at 20 m/s using the formula

$$\text{distance travelled} = \text{average speed} \times \text{time}$$

iii) What happens to the kinetic energy lost by the locomotive in slowing down?

iv) Would you expect these stopping distances to increase or decrease when the locomotive was pulling a number of carriages? Explain your answer.

v) Which of the formulae below relates the stopping distance to the speed of the locomotive? ($s =$ stopping distance, $v =$ speed)
1) $s = 0.5\,v$
2) $s^2 = 4\,v$
3) $s = 4\,v^2$
4) $s = 0.4\,v^2$
5) $2.5\,s = v^2$

5.1.5 Mass and Momentum

1 Two identical space vehicles (each of mass 500 kg) are at rest, one on the surface of the Moon and the other on Mercury. (Gravitational field strengths: Moon 1.6 N/kg, Mercury 3.6 N/kg.)

a) What would be the mass of each vehicle as measured at each site?

b) What would the weight of each vehicle be?

c) Richard believes that the force needed to give the vehicle a horizontal acceleration of 1 m/s² is greater on Mercury than on the Moon. David thinks that the force required would be the same in each case. Who is correct, and why?

2 Copy and complete the following paragraph which compares **mass** and **weight** using the words in the list below.

<blockquote>
matter   mass   force   velocity   60   100
</blockquote>

_____ is measured in kilograms, and represents the amount of _____ present in an object. It can also be described as the resistance of an object to changes in _____. If you took an object of mass 60 kg (as measured on Earth) to the Moon, it would have a mass of _____ kg. Weight is an example of a _____. On Earth, a person with a mass of 60 kg is pulled towards the centre of the Earth with a force of 600 N. On the Moon, the same person would weigh _____ N, because the acceleration due to gravity there is approximately one-sixth of that on Earth.

3 Given an inertia balance (wig-wag) and a timer, together with three rods each of mass 0.10 kg, explain how you would find the mass of another rod, thought to be about 0.15 kg.

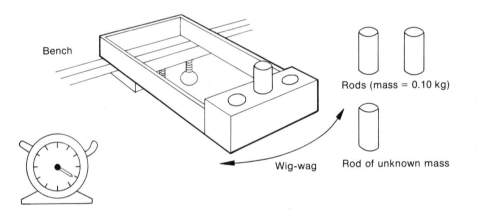

Bench

Rods (mass = 0.10 kg)

Rod of unknown mass

Wig-wag

4 The momentum, p, of an object is given by the expression

$$p = mv$$

where m is the mass of the object in kg and v is its velocity in m/s.

a) Which of the following units is momentum measured in?

      kg/m/s   **kg.m/s**   **kg/m.s**   **kg.m.s**

b) Calculate the momentum of the following objects:
  i) A ball, mass 100 g, travelling at 10 m/s.

  ii) An athlete, mass 60 kg, running at 8 m/s.

  iii) A car, mass 900 kg, moving at 30 m/s.

5 Two asteroids are on a collision course in deep space. One is approaching the other at a relative velocity of 4 km/s as shown.

Mass = 9×10^{14} kg   4 km/s   Mass = 6×10^{14} kg

Assuming that the asteroids form a single larger body after collision, calculate:

a) the mass of the body

b) the velocity of the body

6 a) A 500 g cannon fires a cannon ball (mass 20 kg) horizontally at 50 m/s. Calculate the velocity of recoil of the cannon.

500 kg   20 kg   Recoil   250 m/s

(Formula: momentum = mass × velocity.)

b) Ignoring effects due to air resistance, what is:

i) the horizontal component of the velocity when the cannon ball hits the ground?

ii) the shape of the curved path followed by the cannon ball?

7 After launch, a firework rocket reaches a height of 50 m. As it reaches its maximum height, it breaks into three fragments. Two of the fragments travel in directions X and Y. Which of the directions marked A, B and C must represent the direction of the third fragment? Explain your choice.

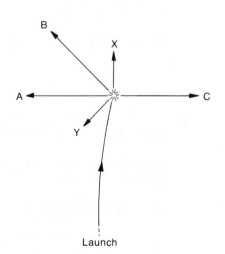

5.1.6 **Structures and Materials**

1 Two similar metal bars, made of steel and aluminium, are tested by hanging weights from their mid-points as shown in the diagram.

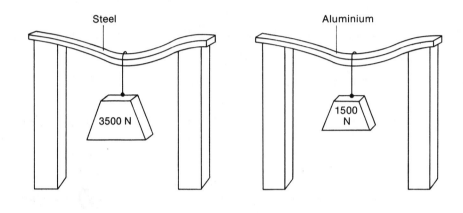

Steel		**Aluminium**	
Mass	7.9 kg	Mass	2.7 kg
Melting point	1535 °C	Melting point	650 °C
Cost	£35/tonne	Cost	£950/tonne

The bars are shown with just enough weight to cause bending.

a) The metal used to make bridges needs to be able to bend slightly without breaking. Give *two* reasons why steel would be better than aluminium for making bridges.

b) Why would aluminium be better than steel to use in making a space station?

2 In a structure, a component under **tension** is called a **tie**, while a component under **compression** is called a **strut**.

Copy the diagrams of structures below and for each one say whether it shows compression or tension, and whether it is a strut or a tie. (The arrows represent forces.)

a) →☐←

b) ←☐→

3 For each structure a) to d), state whether the labelled components (A, B and C) are
struts or ties. See the previous question for definitions of struts and ties.

a)

b)

c)

d)

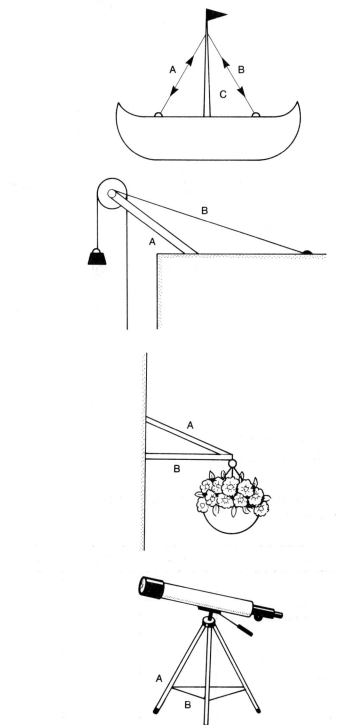

4   The diagram below, which is not to scale, shows the atoms in a block of a solid material. A load is resting on the surface of the block.

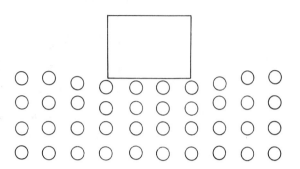

a)   What holds the atoms together in a solid?

b)   How does the solid support the weight of the load?

c)   What would happen if the weight of the load was increased continuously?

5   a)   Explain what is meant by
          i) a strong material
          ii) a flexible material

b)   Copy and complete the following table by putting a tick under the words which describe each material:

Materials	Strong	Weak	Flexible	Stiff
Bone				
Concrete (in compression)				
Glass				
Paper				
Rubber				
Steel				
Wood				

6 Paving stones are made of a composite material. They often crack with no visible sign that this is about to happen, as pressure on a slab from above causes a crack to appear on the underside.

a) i) What is a composite material?

ii) Which composite is used to make paving stones?

b) Using the formula

$$\text{pressure} = \frac{\text{force}}{\text{area}}$$

calculate the pressure exerted when a man (weight 800 N) stands on a paving stone (total area of feet in contact with the stone 0.02 m²).

c) i) Which surface of the paving stone is under compression?

ii) Which surface of the paving stone is under tension?

iii) Is the material stronger in compression or tension? Explain your answer.

7 a) The ties in the Forth Rail Bridge are conventional lattice girders, while the struts are made from tubular steel components, up to 3.6 m in diameter.

i) What is the advantage of using tubular steel components compared with solid steel of the same diameter?

ii) What is the advantage of using tubular components over those made from the same amount of material in solid form?

b) i) Name the tubular components which support plant stems.

ii) Draw a transverse section of a non-woody stem to show how these components are arranged.

iii) What forces do plant stems have to withstand?

c) List two advantages of hollow bones to birds.

8 The graphs below show how two materials behave when stretched.

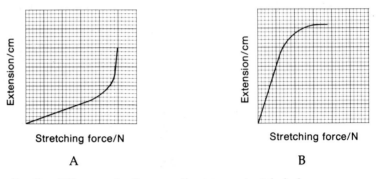

A   B

a) Describe the difference in the way the two materials behave.

b) Which one is steel and which one is rubber?

c) Why is it important for an engineer involved in designing a bridge to know how metals behave under tension?

5.2 ENERGY

5.2.1 Fuels and Energy Resources

1   The graph below shows a 'depletion curve' for world reserves of coal, an important fossil fuel.

Consumption/10^9 tonnes per year

Year

World consumption of coal in thousands of millions of tonnes per year for the period 1900–2900

a)   What is a fossil fuel?

b)   Name *two* other fossil fuels.

c)   Use the graph to find:
i) the predicted consumption of coal in the year 2000
ii) the year when consumption is predicted to reach a maximum value

d)   i) Give *one* reason for the predicted increase in coal consumption between the years 2000 and 2100
ii) Give *one* reason for the predicted fall in coal consumption between the years 2400 and 2500.

e)   Explain what is meant by describing coal as a 'non-renewable' energy source.

2 Read the passage which is about energy from biomass and answer the following questions.

> With fossil fuels running out, the world needs renewable energy sources that can be re-made as fast as they are used up. Plant material called **biomass** is a good renewable energy source.
>
> Biomass energy is particularly important in developing countries, which often do not have their own fossil fuels and cannot afford to buy them. Examples of biomass fuels are wood, charcoal, alcohol, vegetable oil and biogas (methane).
>
> A tenth of the energy stored by the process of photosynthesis could provide all the world's energy needs.

a) What is the ultimate source of energy in the world?

b) What is a renewable energy source?

c) What is biomass?

d) Give *four* examples of biomass fuels.

e) Why is biomass energy particularly important in developing countries?

f) Why are tropical countries generally better able to produce biomass fuels than cool countries like Britain?

3 Read this short passage about the production of biogas, then answer the following questions.

> When vegetable and animal matter rots in the absence of air, a gas is given off. The gas is usually about 60% methane, the rest being mostly carbon dioxide. This biogas is a good fuel, particularly for cooking, heating and lighting in the home.
>
> Rubbish is often tipped into holes in the ground. This is called landfill. This rubbish will also generate biogas.

a) Why is the gas called biogas?

b) Why is biogas particularly easy to make on farms?

c) What use can be made of the solid material left behind in the digestor?

d) What type of organisms are responsible for producing biogas from vegetable and animal matter?

e) Design and draw a suitable method for collecting biogas from a landfill site.

f) What kinds of household rubbish would work best at producing biogas?

4 Read this passage, which is about the use of alcohol as a fuel, then answer the following questions.

> Sugar cane is a fast-growing tropical plant. The sugar it provides can be **fermented** to make alcohol. Alcohol can be used instead of petrol in cars. It is often mixed with petrol to produce **gasohol.**
>
> After the sugar cane has been crushed to remove the sugar, a woody material called **bagasse** is left. This can be used as a solid fuel to provide heat for the **distillation** of the fermented sugar. It can also be used to generate electricity for the sugar factory. In some countries the sugar factories are able to produce electricity for the national grid as well.
>
> Bagasse can also be used in ways other than burning it. A gas, similar to natural gas, can be made from it. It can also be used to make paper and card and building materials such as hardboard.

a) By what process is the Sun's energy converted into chemical energy in the sugar?

b) Explain the meaning of the words 'fermented' and 'distillation'.

c) What is
   i) gasohol?
   ii) bagasse?

d) Why is it particularly advantageous for Brazil to produce fuel in this way?

e) List *three* uses of bagasse.

f) To grow enough sugar cane to replace all liquid fuels with alcohol, Brazil would have to create new farmland by clearing parts of the Amazon jungle. What problems would this cause?

5   Wind-powered electric generators (aerogenerators) are used to produce energy on a small scale at remote sites, or in an emergency when the main source of electricity fails. At present, the blades of a wind-powered generator can be up to 50 metres in diameter and the electrical power produced can reach up to 1 000 000 watts in favourable conditions.

50 m

An aerogenerator

a)   Which of the sites 1–3 shown on the map opposite would be suitable for an aerogenerator?

b)   i) A conventional power station has an output of 2 000 000 000 W. How many aerogenerators would be needed to produce this amount of power?

ii) What effect would this number of aerogenerators have on the area in which they were built?

iii) Give *two* reasons why aerogenerators are not used for large scale electricity production in Britain.

c)   What device could be used to convert the energy of the blades into electricity?

d)   i) Explain why it is less harmful to the environment to generate electricity from 'alternative' energy sources such as wind power than from fossil fuels burnt in conventional power stations.

ii) Briefly describe the use of geothermal energy and one other alternative energy source.

6 The table below shows the energy consumption in millions of joules per passenger per kilometre for various types of transport.

Type of transport	Energy consumption (MJ/passenger/km)
Motorcycle (average)	0.72
Private car (average)	1.80
Bus	0.90
Diesel train	1.00

a) Which is the most energy efficient form of transportation?

b) List *two* factors which cause the energy consumption of private vehicles to be particularly variable.

c) What is the total energy consumption for transporting 20 people over a distance of 10 km using:

   i) 5 private cars?   ii) 1 bus?

d) Apart from energy conservation, give *one* other reason why the use of public transport should be encouraged.

e) Which would you expect to be more energy efficient, a ferry boat or an aeroplane, and why?

f) Explain how the shape of a vehicle can affect its energy efficiency.

7 The diagram shows a new idea for transferring energy from sea waves. An air-tight box is built on the edge of the sea. An entrance at the bottom of the box lets the sea flow in and out. At the top of the box is another opening which is connected to a turbine generator.

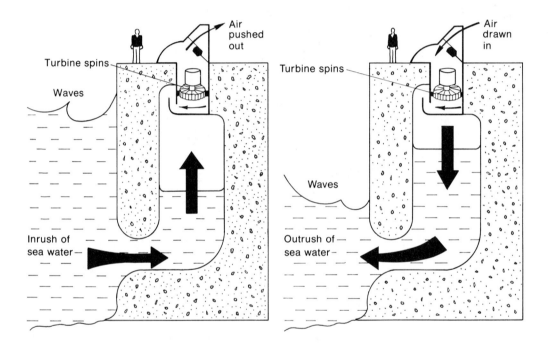

a) Explain, as fully as you can, how energy is transferred from the waves to produce electricity.

b) Part of the energy from the waves is not transferred into electricity. Suggest *two* reasons for this.

c) The turbine is specially made so that it spins in the same direction whether the air is going into or coming out of the box chamber. What advantage does this design have over a turbine that spins only when water is coming into the chamber?

d) Suggest *one* advantage and *one* disadvantage of building such a device on a coast where there are very large waves.

e) List *two* advantages that a generator powered by waves has over one that uses a fossil fuel.

8 Read the passage below and answer the questions which follow.

> Electric vehicles are rarely seen on our roads, with the exception of milk floats. Although the efficiency of a typical electric car (70%) is greater than that of a petrol vehicle (25%), the 'energy density' of lead/acid batteries used in electric cars is only 140 kJ/kg compared to 46 MJ/kg for petrol. To overcome this disadvantage, a new low-mass sodium/sulphur battery has been developed which is capable of storing the same amount of energy even though it has only 20% of the mass of the lead/acid type. The vehicles involved differ in mass also, since electric motors are up to five times heavier than the equivalent petrol variety. However, electric cars are believed to be less harmful to the environment as they do not release nitrogen oxides into the atmosphere.

a) Write down *two* advantages of electric cars over petrol cars, and *one* disadvantage.

b)   i) Explain what 'energy density' means.
    ii) What are the energy densities of electric and petrol cars as measured in J/kg?
    iii) What is the energy density of a sodium/sulphur battery, measured in kJ/kg?

c) In spite of being much less efficient, petrol vehicles can travel much further on one tank of petrol than an electric vehicle can on one charge. Why is this?

d) How long would it take to charge a 480 kJ capacity electric vehicle on a 240 V/5 A supply?

(Electrical energy transferred, E, is found from the expression

$$E = ItV$$

where I is the current (A), t is the time (s) and V is the voltage (V).)

e) Give *two* reasons why electric vehicles are suitable for use as milk floats.

f) Describe *one* consequence of the release of nitrogen oxides into the atmosphere.

g) It has been said that electric vehicles transfer their pollution to the power stations. Explain this statement.

9   1. One uranium-235 nucleus can release 3×10^{-11} J.

  2. 1 kg of uranium-235 contains 3×10^{24} atoms.

  3. 1 kg of coal can produce 3×10^{10} J on combustion.

Use the information provided to calculate the mass of coal needed to produce the same amount of energy as 1 g of uranium-235.

10   Trace the diagram of a nuclear reactor and replace the letters A–F with labels from
the following list:

uranium oxide fuel rods   **boron control rods**   **graphite moderator**
concrete pressure vessel   **steel lining**   **circulating gas**

5.2.2 Waves

1   a)   What is the difference between longitudinal and transverse waves?

   b)   Draw up a table with the headings *Longitudinal waves* and *Transverse waves* and
place each of the following in the appropriate column.

radio waves   **compression waves in a spring**   **sound waves**
water waves   **light waves**   **X-rays**   **gamma rays**

2 The diagram below shows a ship at anchor in rough seas. The water waves are transverse waves.

Direction of wave motion

a) i) Copy the diagram.

ii) Describe how the ship would move as the waves go by.

b) The diagram below shows a long spring vibrating along its length. This is an example of a longitudinal wave. Describe the motion of the part of the spring marked with a black dot as the waves go by.

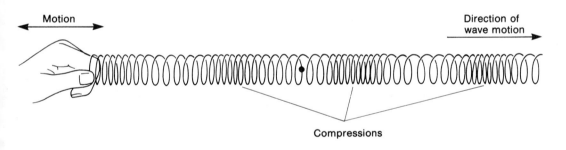

Motion

Direction of wave motion

Compressions

3 Copy the diagram of a wave in a length of rope and add labels which identify the wavelength, the amplitude and a wave crest.

4 Copy and complete the following diagrams of ripple tank experiments to show the wave patterns produced as the experiments progress:

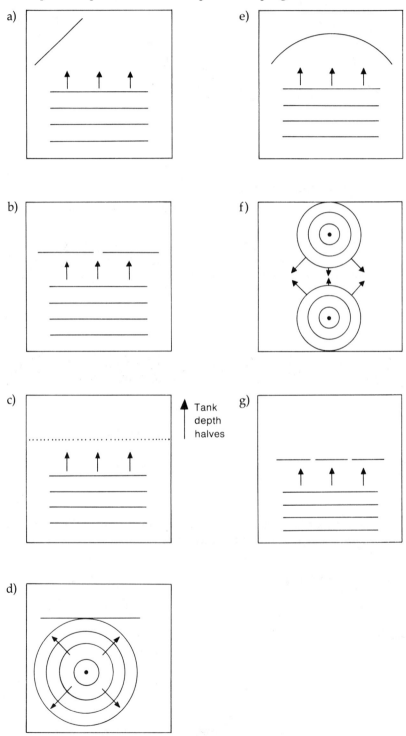

a)

e)

b)

f)

c)   Tank   g)
                                     depth
                                     halves

d)

5   Water waves travel more slowly in shallow water.

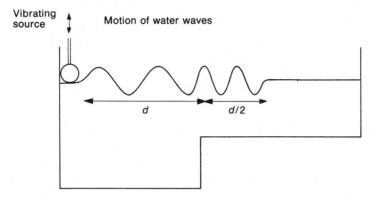

In the example shown, the distances travelled in equal times are marked. Describe what happens to

a)   the velocity

b)   the wavelength

c)   the frequency

d)   the amplitude

of the waves as they enter the shallow water.

6   Some of the following statements about waves are true, some false. Copy out each one, correcting those that are wrong.

a)   Waves can be longitudinal or transverse.

b)   Light is an example of a longitudinal wave.

c)   The amplitude of a water wave is the distance from crest to crest.

d)   Waves are a means of transferring energy without transferring matter.

e)   The frequency of a wave can be found by dividing the wavelength by the wave velocity.

f)   In the passage of a longitudinal wave through air, the molecules vibrate in a direction parallel to the direction of wave travel.

g)   Two progressive transverse waves can interfere to produce a standing wave.

h)   Points of zero displacement in a standing wave are called nodes.

7 Copy and complete the wave formula:

$$\text{velocity} = \underline{\hspace{2cm}} \times \text{wavelength}$$

Use it to carry out the following calculations.

a) Find the velocity of sound waves in air which have a frequency of 900 Hz and a wavelength of 0.35 m.

b) Calculate the wavelength of sound waves in water, having a frequency of 700 Hz and velocity of 1.43 km/s.

c) Find the frequency of sound waves in a steel rod, if the waves have a wavelength of 10 cm and travel at 5.5 km/s.

d) Calculate the wavelength of red light which has a frequency of 5.0×10^{14} Hz and velocity 3.0×10^8 m/s.

e) Calculate the time interval between waves on a surfing beach if the waves have a wavelength of 48 m and travel at 6 m/s.

f) Find the wavelength of radio waves with frequency 5×10^8 Hz and velocity 3×10^8 m/s.

8 Select one of the wave phenomena below which is responsible for each effect described in a)–e).

reflection   refraction   diffraction

a) Two parallel rays of light are brought to a focus by a convex lens.

b) An echo is heard when a gun is fired at some distance from cliffs.

c) Light from the Sun remains visible for a short while after the Sun has set below the horizon.

d) Circular waves are produced when parallel water waves meet a barrier with a small central slit.

e) When a source of white light is viewed through a glass plate on which fine lines have been etched (say 80 lines per millimetre), a series of rainbow patterns can be seen.

5.2.3 Energy Transfer

1 Copy the formulae below and include the correct units chosen from the list:

watts   seconds   newtons   metres   joules

a)   work done   =   force   × distance moved
       (_____)   (_____)   (_____)

    b)   power   = $\dfrac{\text{work done (_____)}}{\text{time taken (_____)}}$

        (_____)

2 List ten examples of energy transfer

3 Copy the statements below, choosing the correct words from this list to fill in the blanks.

          newton   force   created   watt   power   work   metre
          conservation   destroyed   changed

a) Energy transferred is equal to the _____ done.

b) One joule is the work done when a force of one _____ acts over a distance of one _____ (in the direction of the _____).

c) Energy cannot be _____ or _____ but it can be _____ from one form to another. This is the principle of _____ of energy.

d) _____ is the rate of doing work.

e) A rate of doing work of one joule per second is equal to one _____.

4 a) A man of mass 80 kg climbs a flight of stairs to get from the ground floor to his second floor flat. Each step is 0.2 m high and there are 30 steps. How much work does he do against gravity?

    b) If it takes him 10 s to run up the stairs, how much power does he develop?

    c) What energy changes are involved in running up the stairs?

    d) The next day he takes the lift instead of using the stairs. If the lift has a mass of 250 kg, how much work is done by the motor which drives the lift?

5 Copy and complete the following table showing some energy conversions in a motor car.

Device	Conversion
Battery	_____ → electrical energy
Headlamps	electrical energy → _____
Horn	_____ → sound energy
Brakes	kinetic energy → _____
Engine	thermal energy → _____

6 Match the methods of heat transfer with their correct definitions:

Method of heat transfer	*Definition*
Conduction	The transfer of energy by circulation of the material due to differences in temperature.

Convection	The transfer of energy by means of electro-magnetic waves without the need of a material medium.
Radiation	The transfer of energy through a material, from points of high temperature to points of low temperature, without the movement of the material itself.

7 Copy the diagram of a vacuum flask and explain carefully how the design of the flask prevents heat transfer between the contents of the flask and the surroundings.

8 Explain the following observations.

a) Feathers and fur are very good at keeping birds and animals warm.

b) The cooling unit is placed at the top of a freezer, but the heating element in a water tank is at the bottom.

c) It is more comfortable to wear white clothes in the summer than black clothes.

d) People suffering from hypothermia are wrapped in a plastic sheet coated with shiny aluminium.

e) In cold conditions it is better to wear several layers of thin clothing rather than one layer of thick clothing.

f) Newspaper used to keep fish and chips hot will also keep ice cream cold.

g) A fire fighting suit is bright and shiny.

h) The inside of a greenhouse is warmer than the outside.

i) Food in a chest freezer will stay frozen even if the lid is left open for several hours. Food in an upright freezer will soon begin to defrost if the door is left open.

j) During vigorous exercise your face becomes very red.

9   Electric storage heaters operate on cheap electricity supplied at night, which is used to heat concrete blocks. During the following day, heat stored in the blocks is transferred to the room.

Concrete is a suitable material for this application because it has a high density and is good at storing thermal energy. The energy stored in warming 10 kg concrete through 1 °C (costing 0.01 p) will raise the temperature of 1 m³ of air by 7 °C. If the concrete was replaced by the same mass of water, however, the energy stored in raising the water temperature by 1 °C (costing 0.03 p) would raise the temperature of 1 m³ of air by 35 °C.

An electric storage heater

a)   Explain why electricity is cheaper at night.

b)   The larger the specific heat capacity of a material, the better it is at storing thermal energy. Would you expect concrete to have a larger specific heat capacity than water? Explain your answer.

c)   Using the formula

$$\text{mass} = \text{volume} \times \text{density}$$

calculate the volume occupied by 10 kg concrete (density 2400 kg/m³).

d)   Use the same formula to calculate the volume occupied by 10 kg water.

e)   Give *two* reasons why water is not used in preference to concrete in electric storage heaters.

f)   Do storage heaters warm a room mainly by conduction, convection or radiation?

10   The diagram below shows some of the main energy losses from a home in Britain.

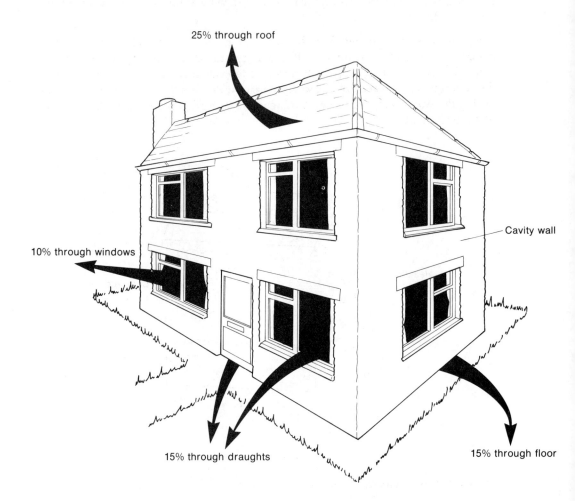

25% through roof

10% through windows

Cavity wall

15% through draughts

15% through floor

a)   Energy is also lost through the cavity walls.

   i) What percentage is this of the total energy loss?

   ii) Explain how filling the cavity with foam reduces heat loss.

b)   Suggest *two* reasons why the rooms on the north side of the house may be colder than those on the south side.

c)   The owner of the house decides to improve insulation by either fitting double glazing or insulating the roof.

   i) Which of the two methods would save more on fuel bills? Explain your answer.

   ii) What additional benefit would be gained from fitting double glazing?

    d) Explain how each of the following reduces fuel costs:

       i) fitting aluminium foil behind radiators

       ii) blocking off unused fire places and their chimneys

       iii) lagging the hot water cylinder

       iv) laying carpets

    e) Explain why energy conservation is an important issue on a global scale.

11 Christopher is planning to go walking in the Scottish mountains in winter. He has obtained samples of two materials used by different manufacturers to make anoraks.

Design a simple experiment which he could carry out to find out which anorak he should buy to keep him the warmest. Include details of how he should carry out his experiment, making sure it is a fair test, and how he should record and interpret his results.

12 The list below shows the specific heat capacity of some materials.

Material	Specific heat capacity (J/kg/°C)
Air	900
Alcohol	2500
Aluminium	900
Copper	400
Cotton	1400
Glass	670
Ice	2100
Iron	450
Polystyrene	1300
Water	4200

    a) Explain the term 'specific heat capacity'.

    b) What units is specific heat capacity measured in?

    c)   i) Draw a column graph of the specific heat capacities given in the list above.

       ii) Which material needs the most energy to warm it up through a given temperature change?

       iii) Which material is the easiest to warm up through a given temperature change?

    d) How much energy would be needed to warm up
       i) 3 kg of water by 10 °C?

       ii) 500 g of aluminium from 20 °C to 50 °C?

13 Copy the information below which is about **machines** using words from this list to fill in the blanks:

>   **effort   energy   forces   load**

Machines help us to apply _____ more easily. A machine is a mechanism for transferring _____. The force applied to a machine is called the _____. Something called the _____ is moved by the machine. Ideally a large _____ is moved by a small _____.

14 Make a list of the levers you can find in your home. For each one say whether it is a *force multiplier* or a *distance multiplier*.

15 a) Copy and complete these formulae:

>   i) _____ $= \dfrac{\text{load}}{\text{effort}}$

>   ii) velocity ratio (VR) $= \dfrac{\text{distance moved by _____}}{\text{distance moved by _____}}$

   b)   i) A machine has a mechanical advantage of 10. What does this mean?

       ii) A machine has a velocity ratio of 3. What does this mean?

       iii) Write down *two* formulae which can be used to calculate the percentage efficiency of a machine.

   d) A machine has an efficiency of 50%. What does this mean?

   e) Explain why it is necessary to keep the moving parts of a machine well lubricated.

16

Effort
220 N

Load
400 N

The pulley system shown above is used to move a load of 400 N. The effort moves through a distance of 1.0 m while the load moves through a distance of 0.5 metres.

Calculate:

a)   the mechanical advantage of the pulley

b)   the velocity ratio of the pulley

c)   the work done in lifting the load (Formula: work done = force × distance moved)

d)   the work done by the effort

e)   the efficiency of the pulley

17   Using a block and tackle, an engine is hoisted out of a car. The engine has a mass (m) of 400 kg and is raised to a height (h) of 1.5 metres.

a)   Use the expression

$$\text{work done} = m.g.h$$

to calculate the work done in raising the engine through 1.5 m against gravity. (g = 10 N/kg)

b)   The mechanic operating the block and tackle pulled the chain through 20 m with a force of 1600 N. Use the expression

$$\text{work done} = F.s$$

to calculate the work done by the mechanic in pulling the chain with force F through distance s.

c)   Use the expression

$$\% \text{ efficiency } = \frac{\text{work done (output)}}{\text{energy supplied (input)}}$$

to calculate the percentage efficiency of the block and tackle.

d)   What is the main cause of the low efficiency?

e)   Explain why it is useful in this case to have such a low efficiency.

18   A heat engine works on the principle that some of the heat produced by a source can be converted into mechanical work:

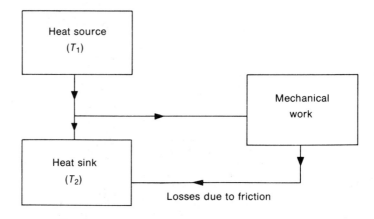

The theoretical efficiency of the heat engine is given by the expression

$$\% \text{ efficiency } = \frac{T_1 - T_2}{T_1} \times 100 \quad (T \text{ in kelvins})$$

a)   How is the high 'source' temperature achieved in a motor car engine?

b)   What is the 'heat sink' referred to in the diagram?

c)   Taking the external temperature to be 20 °C (293 K), calculate the theoretical efficiency of a heat engine with the following inlet (source) temperatures:
i)   100 °C (373 K)
ii) 1000 °C (1273 K)

d)   In practice the efficiency of a heat engine operating at 1000 °C is approximately 50% at best. Compare this with your answer to part c) ii) and account for any difference.

e)   Why is it not possible to operate a heat engine at temperatures much above 1000 °C?

19 a) Use the formula

$$\text{power} = \frac{\text{energy transferred or work done}}{\text{time taken}}$$

to calculate the power developed during each of the following examples:

i) A girl running steadily to the top of a flight of stairs in 30 s. She gains 4000 J of potential energy.

ii) An electric bar heater which releases 60 kJ of energy in 1 min.

iii) A pulley which raises a load of 1000 N through 2 m in 5 s.

iv) A space probe radio which radiates 12 J in 1 min.

v) The Sun, which releases 1.2×10^{34} J in 1 year.

b) A light bulb is marked 60 W. Explain what this means.

20 Rotary motion can be transferred from one shaft to another using a belt on pulley wheels or a sprocket and chain system.

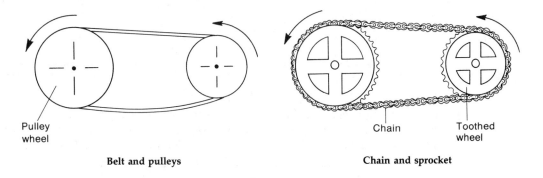

Pulley
wheel

Chain

Toothed
wheel

Belt and pulleys   **Chain and sprocket**

a) Write down *one* advantage and *one* disadvantage of each mechanism.

b) An exercise bicycle uses a chain and sprocket mechanism to drive a flywheel. The user must work against a frictional force which can be varied by adjusting the tension in the steel band. (See the diagram on the next page.)

i) Explain why the sprocket and chain mechanism is the better choice for use on the exercise bicycle.

ii) List *two* safety problems that might arise when using the cycle. What modifications would make it safer to use?

iii) How can the frictional force be calculated from the readings on the force-meters?

iv) What measurements must be taken, in addition to the friction applied, in order to calculate the energy transferred during a period of exercise on the machine?

c) A chart on the cycle can be used to convert the value of the frictional force applied (N) and revolutions per minute (r.p.m.) of the flywheel into power output (W). Part of the chart is shown below, with one of the values omitted.

Frictional force (N)	Power output (W)	
	40 r.p.m.	80 r.p.m.
20	16	32
40	32	
60	48	96
80	64	128
100	80	160

i) What is the power output needed to maintain 80 r.p.m. against a frictional force of 40 N?

ii) How much energy is transferred when cycling for 1 min at 80 r.p.m. against a frictional force of 40 N?
(Formula: energy transferred = power output × time.)

iii) Calculate the circumference of the flywheel friction drum.
(Formula: work done = force × distance.)

5.3 SOUND AND MUSIC

5.3.1 Sound and Hearing

1 a) Copy and complete the passage below choosing words from the following list to fill the gaps. (You may use a word more than once or not at all.)

> air   empty   energy   longitudinal   molecules   pulled
> pushed   transverse   vibrate   waves

> Sound is a form of _____. It is produced when an object is made to _____. It travels in _____ through any substance, solid, liquid or gas. Sound can travel through _____ but not through _____ space. This is because _____ in the air can be made to _____. The molecules are alternately _____ together and _____ apart to form the sound _____. Sound waves are examples of _____ waves.

b) Explain why astronauts in space cannot talk directly to each other but must communicate by radio.

c) Through which type of substance, solid, liquid or gas, does sound travel most quickly? Give a reason for your answer.

d) Try to explain how the beating of a drum produces sound waves in the air.

2 The diagram below shows the sound waves produced by a vibrating tuning fork.

Vibrating tuning fork

a) Copy the wave pattern on one side of the tuning fork.

b) Mark

    i) a point A where the air is compressed

    ii) a point B where the air is rarefied

    iii) a distance C which represents the wavelength of the sound

c) The diagrams below represent the air molecules at the points A and B you have marked.

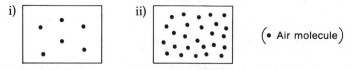

i)   ii) $\left(\bullet \text{ Air molecule} \right)$

Copy the diagrams and say which point A or B they represent.

d) Copy the statement below, choosing only the correct alternative i), ii) or iii) to complete it.

When a sound wave passes by, in this direction →, an air molecule

   i) oscillates at right angles to the direction of the wave •↕

   ii) oscillates in the same direction as the wave motion •↔

   iii) moves with the wave •→

3 Copy these sentences, choosing only the correct alternative from inside the brackets.

a) When the (amplitude/frequency) of vibrations increases, the sound produced becomes (louder/softer).

b) When the (amplitude/frequency) of vibrations increases, the pitch of the sound becomes (higher/lower).

c) When the frequency of vibrations is (changing/constant) a sound is heard as a musical note with a fixed (loudness/pitch). For example, middle C has an (amplitude/frequency) of 256 vibrations per second (Hz).

4 Sound level is measured in units called **decibels** (dB). The table below shows the approximate sound level of some sources of noise, measured at a 'working' distance.

Source	Sound level (dB)
Minimum sound that can be heard	0
Whisper	30
Conversation	60
Heavy traffic	90
Pneumatic drill	100
Low flying jet aircraft	130
Pain threshold	140
(At 100–110 dB conversation becomes impossible.)	

a) Using the information in the table to help you, estimate the sound level of

   i) a telephone ringing

   ii) a loudspeaker at a disco

   iii) a person shouting at the top of his voice

b) In schools close to busy airports, lessons are frequently disrupted by the noise from low flying aircraft. Describe one way of soundproofing classrooms against this noise.

5 If a sound level is higher than 80 dB, the ears may be damaged.

Kate wants to find out how far away from a noisy machine she can sit for a long time without risking damage to her ears. She took sound level meter readings at different distances from the machine. These are her results.

Distance/m	1	2	3	5	7	8	10	14
Sound level/dB	96	90	86	82	89	78	76	73

a)   i) Plot a graph of these results. Label the axes as shown.

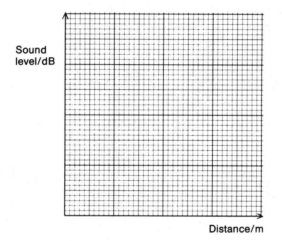

Sound level/dB

Distance/m

ii) Kate has made a mistake in one of her readings. Which one is incorrect?

iii) Suggest what you think the reading on the sound level meter should have been at that point.

b) Use the graph to answer the following questions.

i) What is the sound level 4 m from the machine?

ii) How far away from the machine is the sound level 74 dB?

iii) What is the closest Kate can sit to the machine and know that her ears will not be damaged?

6 The noise level and how long it lasts affects whether our hearing may be damaged by noise. Workers in noisy conditions are protected by law. At 90 dB the maximum exposure time allowed is eight hours. At 93 dB it is four hours and at 96 dB it is two hours.

a) What would you expect the time limit to be at 99 dB?

b)   i)   Workers on a production line in a large factory claimed that the noise levels they were exposed to were a danger to health. If you were the safety officer for the factory, how would you decide whether or not their claim was correct?

      ii)   How can workers in noisy conditions be protected against damage to their hearing?

c)   The sound from personal stereos goes directly into the ear. Measurements of the sound level produced by them, at full volume, gave the following results:

         Pop music (Jason Donovan)   110 dB
         Heavy metal music (Jon Bonjovi)   100 dB
         Classical music (Tchaikovsky)   110 dB

      i)   Should the manufacturers of personal stereos issue a health warning with each one? If so, what should it say?

      ii)   What modifications could be made to personal stereos to reduce any risks?

7   a)   Copy this diagram of the **human ear**:

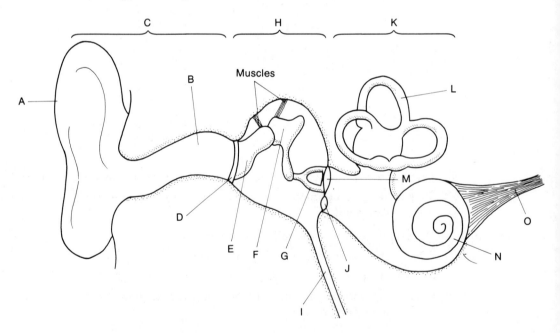

b)   Replace the letters A to O with the correct label from the list below.

        anvil   auditory nerve   cochlea   ear-drum
        Eustachian tube   external ear channel   hammer
        inner ear   middle ear   outer ear   oval window   pinna
        round window   semicircular canals   stirrup

8   a)   Complete the following table:

Part of ear	Is it filled with air or fluid?
Outer ear chamber Middle ear chamber Inner ear chamber	

b)   As sound passes through the ear, it comes into contact with the following structures:

hammer   cochlea   stirrup   anvil   outer ear canal
oval window   ear-drum   auditory nerve   brain   pinna

Starting with the pinna, place these structures in the correct order.

9   a)   Copy and complete this passage about how we hear.

Sound waves are directed into the external ear canal by the _____. The waves cause the _____ to vibrate. The vibrations are amplified many times as they pass along the three tiny ossicles in the _____ ear chamber. The ossicles are called the _____, _____ and _____. The membrane covering the _____ window then vibrates and causes fluid in the cochlea to move. This stimulates tiny sensory _____ cells. A nervous impulse is generated in the _____ nerve. The impulse is carried to the _____, which interprets the message and the sound is heard.

b)   The ear ossicles are held in place by muscles. How does this help to protect the ear from damage by loud noises?

10   a)   i)   Explain how having two ears helps us to judge the direction from which a sound is coming.

ii)   Design an experiment to investigate whether or not this is true.

b)   i)   Many mammals have ear flaps which are moveable, for example horses and dogs. What is the advantage of this?

ii)   How do humans compensate for not having moveable earflaps?

11   The highest pitch which humans can hear has a frequency of 17 000 to 20 000 Hz. It is claimed that the ability to hear high frequency sound decreases with age. Using an audio-signal generator and a loudspeaker, design an experiment to test whether this is true. You should say how you would carry out the investigation, what you would record and how you would present the results.

12 The cochlea is a spiral shape but in the diagram below it is shown straightened out.

a) Explain what is happening at each of the points 1–4 on the diagram, as sound waves enter the ear.

b) The hair cells nearest the oval window are stimulated by high pitched sounds. Lower pitched sounds stimulate hair cells towards the apex of the spiral.

   i) What would be the result of damage to the hair cells in one region of the cochlea?

   ii) This sometimes happens to pop musicians. Can you suggest why?

13 a) What is an echo?

b) Explain why echoes are a nuisance in large concert halls but can sometimes improve the sound in a small concert hall.

c) As part of the planning for a large concert hall experiments were carried out to determine how much sound energy was absorbed by brick, carpet and tiles at various frequencies. The results are given below.

Material	Percentage of sound energy absorbed at a certain frequency		
	125 Hz	500 Hz	2500 Hz
Brick	0.05%	0.02%	0.05%
Tiles	0.8%	0.5%	0.7%
Carpet	0.17%	0.8%	0.9%

   i) Which material is the best absorber at a frequency of 125 Hz?

   ii) Which material is a better absorber at a frequency of 125 Hz?

   iii) If 100 J of sound energy of frequency 500 Hz hits the wall covered with tiles, how much sound energy is reflected?

d) Why do you think such experiments were carried out?

e) Why are wires sometimes stretched across concert halls?

5.3.2 Audio Devices

1 The diagram below is of a **moving coil microphone**. Study the diagram, then copy and complete the passage which follows about how the microphone works. Choose words from the list to fill in the blanks.

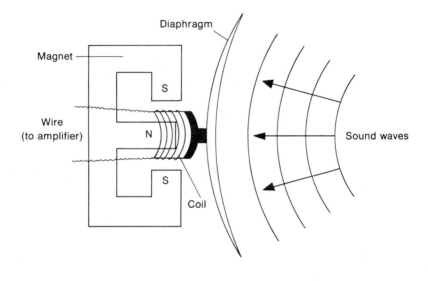

alternating   vibrate   magnetic   loudspeaker
frequencies   ear-drum   coil

The diaphragm of the microphone corresponds to the _____ in the human ear. When sound waves reach the microphone, the diaphragm begins to _____. The coil moves back and forth in the _____ field. A small _____ current is induced in the wire of the _____. When amplified, this current can be used to reproduce the sound using a _____. The moving coil microphone can respond to _____ of sound between 20 Hz and 20 000 Hz, the limits of human hearing.

2 a) Copy the following sentences, choosing only the correct alternatives from inside the brackets.

      i) In a microphone, (electrical/sound) energy is converted into (electrical/sound) energy.

      ii) In a loudspeaker, (electrical/sound) energy is converted into (electrical/sound) energy.

   b) Draw a diagram of a moving coil loudspeaker. Label the magnet, coil, cone and wire from the amplifier.

c)   Why do speakers in hi-fi systems, such as the one shown below, often have one small and one large loudspeaker in the same unit?

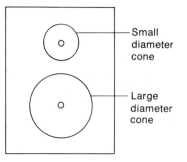

d)   Mr Smith went to a specialist hi-fi shop to buy a pair of loudspeakers. He was prepared to pay a lot of money for a pair with a good bass response. However, the manager of the shop advised him that expensive loudspeakers, able to give notes down to 30 Hz, would be ineffective in his small sitting room. Was this good advice? Explain your answer.

3   One type of telephone earpiece contains a disc, clamped round its edge, with the poles of a magnet close to its centre. Wires carrying the incoming electrical signal are wrapped round the poles of the magnet.

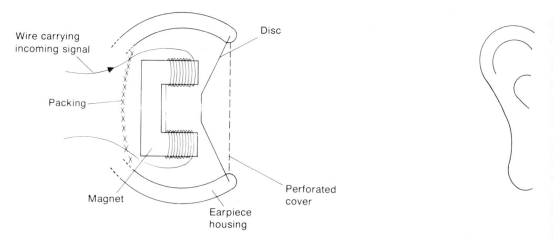

When the current in the wire changes, the degree of magnetisation changes. The disc vibrates as the force of attraction towards the magnet varies rapidly. This reproduces the speech which gave rise to the signal in the wires. An absorbent material is packed behind the disc.

a)   Suggest a suitable material for the disc.

b)   What is the purpose of the packing material?

c)   What type of current – alternating or direct – is present in the coil?

d)   Explain how sound produced by the disc in the unit travels to the ear of the listener.

4 Explain how sound waves are converted into an electrical current by the carbon microphone in the mouthpiece of a telephone.

5 Thousands of kilometres of copper cable carry telephone messages all around the world, but there are problems associated with the use of this network. Using optical fibres to transmit telephone calls can overcome some of these problems.

a) Who invented the telephone and when?

b) Give *one* use of the telephone network in addition to transmitting conversations.

c) Copy and complete the following table which compares the use of optical fibres and copper cables for transmitting telephone messages.

Copper cables	*Optical fibres*

Message carried as an electrical signal
Copper is very expensive
The signal can be upset by electrical
   interference from nearby wires
Fewer messages can be sent down
   one wire (low signal rate)
Cables are heavy and occupy a
   great deal of space
The signal weakens and needs
   amplifying about every 2 km
Cables are easy to join
Cables are not easily broken	

6 A room contains two loudspeakers as shown in the diagram. The loudspeakers are supplied by the same signal generator and operate in phase, producing a note in the audible range.

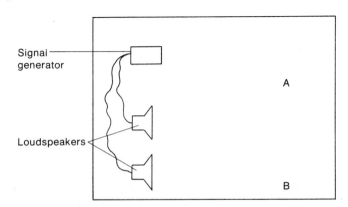

Describe what you would hear when walking from A to B, and explain your answer.

5.3.3 **Vibrations and Musical Instruments**

1 The vibrator produces a wire vibration pattern as shown below.

Draw the pattern produced when:

a)   The frequency of vibration is doubled.

b)   The amplitude of the vibration is doubled.

c)   The string is vibrating at its fundamental frequency.

d)   Describe the effect of each of the changes in parts a), b) and c) on

   i) the pitch of the note produced by the wire

   ii) the loudness of the note produced by the wire

2 Musical instruments produce a note when something is made to vibrate. Match the instruments a)–e) below with their vibrating parts.

Instrument	*Vibrations occur in*
a) **Violin**	a metal rod
b) **Triangle**	a reed
c) **Drum**	air
d) **Flute**	a skin
e) **Saxaphone**	strings

3 When air is blown through the opening at the bottom of an organ pipe, it strikes a sharp edge and a vibration is set up in the air inside the pipe. The loudness of the note produced can be changed by changing the diameter of the pipe, while the pitch of the note depends on the length of the pipe.

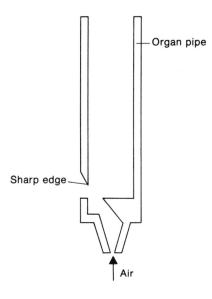

a) Copy and complete the following table showing the effect of a change in the diameter of the pipe on the amplitude, frequency and speed of the sound wave produced.

Change	*Effect of the change on the sound wave*		
	Amplitude	*Frequency*	*Speed*
Increase in pipe diameter			
Decrease in pipe diameter			

b) Would you expect the note produced by a shorter pipe to have a higher or lower pitch? Explain your answer.

4 a) It is easy to recognise sound from different instruments. For example a violin and a piano sound different, even if they are playing the same note. Explain why this is so. In your answer you need to refer to the quality of sound, waveform and harmonics. Use diagrams if you wish.

b) In a violin the strings are mounted on a hollow box. The air in the box vibrates as the strings vibrate and so does the box. Explain what effect this has on the sound produced.

c) Why are low pitched musical instruments usually larger than high pitched ones?

5 A singer, singing a note at a particular frequency, may cause a wine glass to break. Explain how **resonance** causes this to occur.

6

A siren can be produced by directing a jet of compressed air at a set of perforations around the edge of a rotating disc. The air is forced through each hole in turn and produces a series of pulses. The frequency of the note depends on the time interval between the pulses.

a)   Would you expect an increase in the rotation rate to produce a note of higher or lower frequency? Explain your answer.

b)   Suggest one other method of increasing the frequency of the note.

c)   What effect would increasing the velocity of the air jet have on the note produced?

7   A thin metal plate is supported at its centre from below. A small amount of sand is sprinkled on its surface, and a violin bow drawn down the middle of one edge while the plate is touched at one corner and one-quarter of the way in from the corner as shown in the diagram. The sand gathers into the pattern shown and a note is heard.

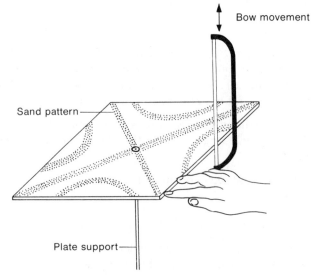

a) What causes the note?

b) Explain why the sand gathers at certain regions on the plate.

c) Suggest one method of making the note louder.

d) A modified experiment is shown below.

Touch at corner and at mid-point

Which of the following is most likely to be part of the pattern formed?

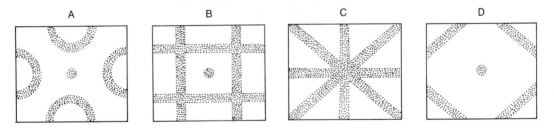

A   B   C   D

8 Two guitar strings, A and B, are stretched across the same pair of bridges as shown. A small V-shaped piece of card is placed over the centre string B. The tension in each string can be varied using keys at one end of the wires.

When string A is plucked, nothing happens to string B. The tension in string A is adjusted and the string is plucked once more. This process is repeated until, at one particular tension setting, string B begins to vibrate when string A is plucked. The piece of card is thrown off string B.

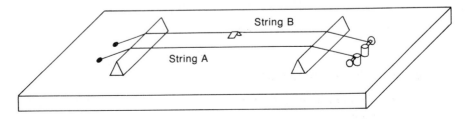

String B

String A

a) Copy the diagram

b) How is the vibration of one string transmitted to the other?

c)   Choose the correct word or words from the list provided to complete the
     following discussion of this experiment. Write out the completed passage.

**resonance   vibration   energy transfer   forced vibration
natural frequency**

The _____ of string B in response to vibrations in string A is an example
of _____. When string A vibrates at the _____ of string B,
_____ occurs and _____ between the strings is very efficient.

5.3.4 Using Sound

1

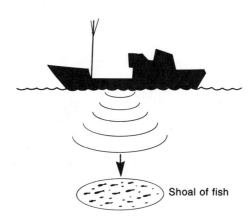

Shoal of fish

The diagram above shows a fishing boat using echo-sounding to detect a shoal of
fish. A short pulse of high frequency sound waves is emitted from the boat, and the
echo from the shoal is detected 0.1 s later. Sound waves travel through sea water at
1500 m/s.

a)   How far below the boat is the shoal of fish? Show your working.

b)   Describe two other situations in which a ship may use echo-sounding.

c)   Why is high frequency sound used?

d)   How might a geologist use echo sounding?

2 a)   What is ultrasound?

b)   Find out how ultrasound is used in the following situations and explain *two* of
     them:

i) by bats and dolphins to help them 'see'

ii) in spectacles for blind people

iii) to detect flaws in pieces of metal

iv) to remove particles of solid material, which sometimes develop into painful stones such as kidney stones, without cutting the patient.

3 Read this passage about the use of ultrasound in pregnancy and answer the questions which follow.

> Ultrasound can be used to produce pictures of unborn babies. This is often referred to as a scan. An ultrasonic transmitter/receiver (the transducer) is moved across the mother's abdomen. This sends ultrasound waves into the body in a narrow beam. Some of the ultrasound is reflected when it comes to a material through which it would have a different speed. The bigger the difference in speed, the bigger the amount of reflection. The receiver changes the reflected waves back into electrical energy and displays them as a spot on an oscilloscope screen. The position of each spot depends on the time delay between the wave being sent out and the reflected wave being received. These spots are built up into a picture on the screen. The pictures enable the size of the baby to be measured. The size of the head is a useful way of determining the baby's age. Abnormalities in the developing skeleton can also be seen. At the lower power levels used, ultrasound has no known harmful effect on any part of the body.

a) For what reasons is a scan usually carried out?

b) Why is ultrasound preferred to X-rays for producing such pictures?

c) How are the ultrasound waves generated?

d) Why are some of the waves reflected?

e) What type of machine is used to display the pictures?

f) The table below gives some information about the speed of sound in different materials.

Material	Speed of sound (m/s)
Muscle	1580
Soft tissue	1500
Bone	4100
Air	340
Saline gel	1515

i) Which one of the following places would cause most reflection of ultrasound?
   A   Where soft tissue meets muscle
   B   Where muscle meets bone
   C   Where saline gel meets soft tissue

ii) The diagram below shows the arrangement normally used for producing
    ultrasound pictures. Why must the transducer be 'coupled' to the patient's
    skin by the saline gel?

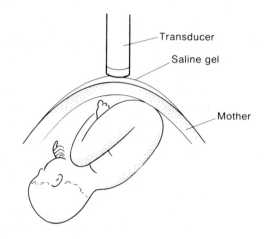

5.4 ELECTRICITY AND MAGNETISM

5.4.1 Static Electricity

1 The diagrams below show one method of charging a gold leaf electroscope using a positively charged rod.

Stage 1
Rod brought close
to plate

Stage 2
With rod in place
the plate is earthed

Stage 3
First the finger
and then the rod
are taken away

  a) Copy the diagrams and add the third one to show what happens when the finger and rod are removed.

  b) Suggest what the rod could be made of and describe one way of charging it.

  c) Draw another set of diagrams to show how the same rod can be used to introduce the opposite electrical charge.

  d) A gold leaf electroscope is given a positive charge. When a charged rod is brought towards the cap of the electroscope, the deflection of the leaf increases. What charge was present on the rod? Explain your answer.

  e) A charged electroscope left in a room for several days slowly loses its charge and the deflection of the leaf falls to zero. Explain this observation.

2 Explain each of the following:

  a) It is difficult to keep
      i) gramophone records   ii) television screens, free of dust

  b) You can make a balloon stick to the ceiling after rubbing the balloon on your clothing.

  c) In dry weather, people walking on nylon carpets may get a shock if they touch a metallic object.

  d) A mirror which has been polished with a dry cloth, on a dry day, soon becomes very dusty.

3 An aircraft is flying above an electrically charged thunder cloud as shown in the diagram.

   a) Copy the diagram and draw in the positions and signs of any charges induced in the aircraft.

   b) Will these induced charges be present when the aircraft eventually lands at its destination, well away from the storm? Explain your answer.

   c) Why is it unlikely that any passengers in the aircraft will be harmed as a direct result of the aircraft being struck by lightning?

Cloud

   d) i) After flying through air for some time in fine weather, a helicopter must be earthed while hovering before ground personnel attach any cargo to the underneath of the helicopter. Why is this necessary?

       ii) How would you earth the helicopter safely?

4

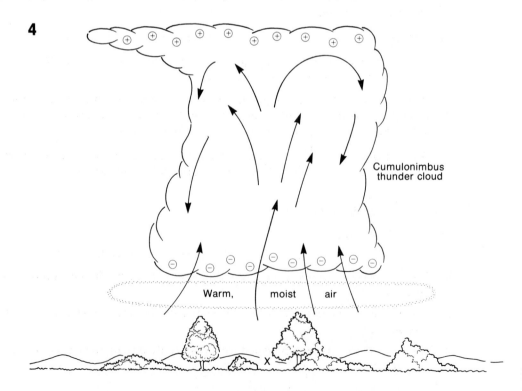

Cumulonimbus thunder cloud

Warm,   moist   air

The diagram opposite shows the air currents in a typical thunder cloud (cumulonimbus). Charges are generated within it, producing lightning.

a) What sign of charge would be induced on the ground at X?

b) Explain how a lightning stroke produces thunder.

c) Under what conditions is the flash of lightning seen at the same time as the thunder clap is heard?

d) The speed of sound in air is 300 m/s. The speed of light in air is 300 000 000 m/s. If a thunder clap is heard 5 seconds after the lightning flash, how far away is the storm?

e) Use the words CONVECTION and FRICTION to explain how charge separation occurs within a cumulonimbus cloud.

5 The experiment below shows that an electric current is a flow of electric charge. The dome and base of a Van de Graaf generator are connected to an ammeter by a pair of charged plates. A polystyrene ball coated with aluminium paint hangs between the plates. When the generator is running, the ball oscillates between the plates, making contact with one then the other, and the ammeter registers a reading.

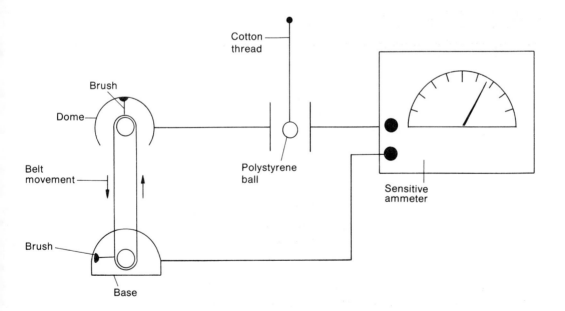

a) Explain how the Van de Graaf machine produces an electric charge.

b) Why does the ball oscillate between the plates?

c) Why must the polystyrene ball be coated in aluminium paint?

d) Copy the following explanation of what is happening in the experiment. Choose words from this list to complete it:

ammeter   electric   flow   plates

The moving ball passes _____ charge between the two _____ and the charge travels round the circuit. As the charge passes through the _____ it registers the _____ of electric charge.

e) Explain why

   i) The ammeter reading increases if the plates are moved closer together.

   ii) The ammeter reading falls to zero if the ball is prevented from moving.

f) If the ball makes contact with each plate twice every second, and transfers 0.000 001 coulombs each oscillation, calculate the current flowing through the ammeter.

$$\left(\text{Formula: current (A)} \ = \ \frac{\text{charge transferred (C)}}{\text{time (s)}} \right)$$

5.4.2 Circuits

1

Power supply

Sample material

Bell

a) Which of the following materials would conduct electricity well and cause the bell to ring when placed in the circuit shown above?

polythene rod	glass rod	sulphur crystal	iron bar
block of wood	copper wire	aluminium foil	zinc rod
rubber band	nickel spatula		

b) Name one solid, non-metallic element which conducts electricity.

2   a)   Name the components shown below.

i)

ii)

iii)

iv)

b)   These components could be used to make an electrical circuit for lighting up a small cupboard. Draw such a circuit, using the standard symbols for each component.

3   The diagram shows a resistor and an ammeter connected to a power supply.

6 V d.c.

A

Resistor

a)   Copy the diagram.

b)   Copy the sentences below choosing only the correct alternatives from inside the brackets.

   i)   When the p.d. of the power supply is increased, the reading on the ammeter (increases/decreases).

   ii)   When the current flowing through the resistor increases, its temperature (increases/decreases).

4 The metal strip and wires shown in the diagram were connected one by one into the circuit drawn below.

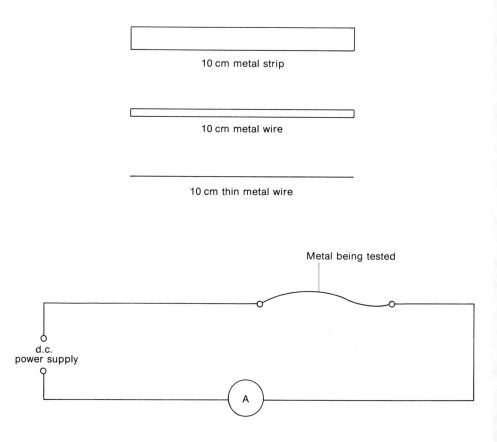

10 cm metal strip

10 cm metal wire

10 cm thin metal wire

Metal being tested

d.c.
power supply

A

a) Copy the circuit diagram, adding the symbol Ⓥ to show how a voltmeter would be placed in the circuit to give the following results.

Metal being tested	Current (A)	Voltage (V)
10 cm metal strip	5	1.5
10 cm metal wire	4.5	1.5
10 cm thin metal wire	4.2	1.5

b)   i) What is the effect of using thinner wire in this circuit?

ii) If a current of 5 A was passed through *each* wire, which would produce the most heat?

c) If each strip is made of the same metal, which one has the highest resistance?

5 a) Suggest where in the home it is a good idea to have two separate switches controlling the same light. Such an arrangement of switches is shown in the circuit diagram below.

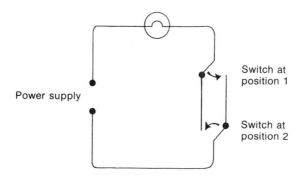

Power supply

Switch at position 1

Switch at position 2

b) Design a circuit which will allow a light to be turned on or off from three positions independently. Describe one situation where this would be useful.

6 Below are six statements about circuits. Sort them into two groups under the following headings:

Series circuits	Parallel circuits

There is only one path for the current.
There are several paths for the current.

The current is not the same at all points in the circuit.
The current is the same at all points in the circuit.

The p.d. across each component is the same.
The p.d. across each component is usually different.

7 a) Choose the most accurate version of Ohm's law from the following list and copy it out:

A The potential difference across a conductor is equal to the resistance of the conductor (in ohms) divided by the current flowing through it (in amperes)

B The current flowing through a metal conductor is directly proportional to the potential difference across its ends at constant temperature.

C The resistance of a conductor is found by dividing the current flowing through it into the potential difference across its ends.

D A metal conductor has a resistance of 1 ohm if a current of 1 ampere flows through it when a potential difference of 1 volt is applied across its ends.

b) The graph below shows how the current flowing through a resistor changes as the potential difference across it is varied.

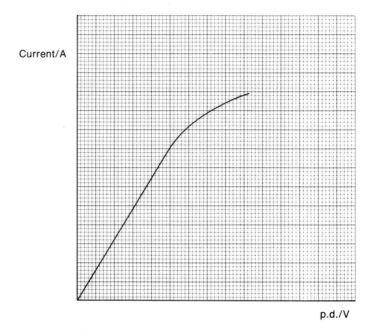

Current/A

p.d./V

i) Copy the graph and label it to show the region where Ohm's law applies.

ii) At the point where the behaviour of the resistor begins to deviate from Ohm's law, does its resistance increase or decrease? Explain your answer.

iii) Suggest an explanation for the deviation from Ohm's law.

c) Measuring the resistance of a light bulb filament does not necessarily lead to a correct calculation of its power rating. Explain why.

8 What is the current shown on the ammeters a)–d) in each circuit shown below. All values are in amperes.

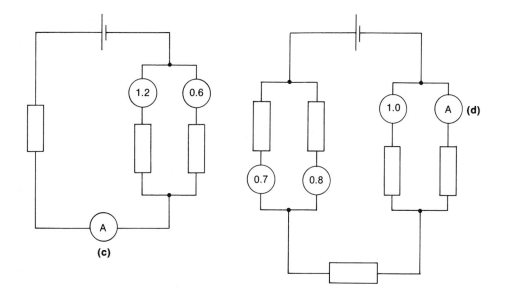

9 What are the readings on the ammeters a)–d) in the circuits shown below? All readings are in ampheres.

(Formula: p.d. across a component = current flowing × resistance of the component.)

10 The diagram below shows three cells connected in parallel.

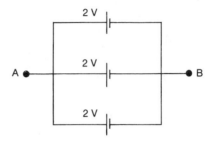

a) What would a voltmeter read when connected across the terminals A and B?

b) Give *two* reasons why it is better to use three cells in this way instead of just one cell.

c) Why should cells *not* be left connected in parallel when not in use?

11 Arrange the following circuits in order of increasing ammeter reading. All resistors, and all cells, are identical.

1.

2.

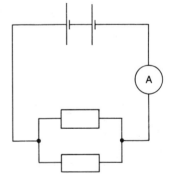

3.

12 Copy the circuits a)–e) below. For each one give the correct voltmeter reading.

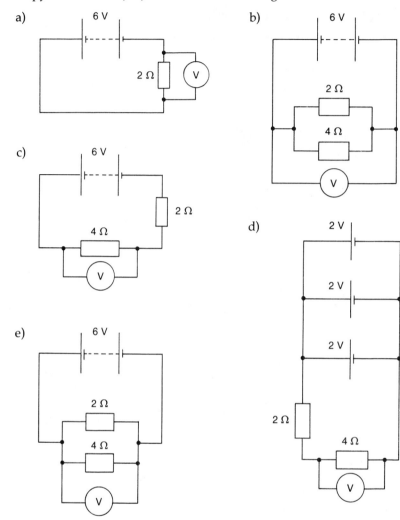

13 In 40 s a charge of 80 C leaves a cell and supplies 240 J of electrical energy to an appliance.

a) What is the cell p.d.?

b) What current was drawn from the cell?

$$\left(\text{Formulae: charge} = \text{current} \times \text{time} \right.$$
$$\left. \text{cell p.d.} = \frac{\text{energy transferred}}{\text{charge}}. \right)$$

5.4.3 Electricity in Use

1

The diagram shows stages in the production and distribution of electricity, from power stations to homes and industry, via the national grid.

a)   What is the main advantage of the grid system?

b)   i) Why is power transmitted at a very high voltage?
     ii) Give *two* reasons why alternating current is essential for this network.

c)   Which of the transformers A–E are step-up transformers?

d)   What is the voltage of the domestic electricity supply?

e)   Why is aluminium preferred to steel for overhead power cables?

f)   Silver is one of the best metallic conductors of electricity.
     i) Give two reasons why thick silver cables would be an advantage in the national grid.
     ii) Give two reasons why silver is not used for overhead power cables.

2 If electricity costs 6.5 p per kWh, calculate

a) the cost of running a 2 kW bar heater for 8 hours

b) the charge for electricity used between the two meter readings below

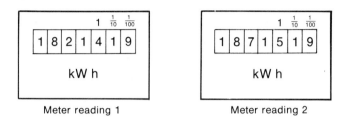

Meter reading 1   Meter reading 2

3 The diagram below shows a standard three-core flex plug.

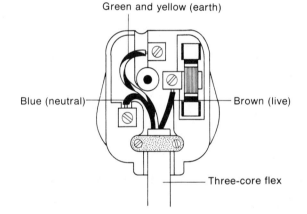

a) What is the purpose of the earth wire (green and yellow)?

b) What type of appliance needs to have an earth wire connected?

c) Why is the fuse connected into the live wire (brown)?

d) i) What happens to the fuse when an unusually large current flows through it?

   ii) How does the fuse protect an appliance?

e) Find out which domestic appliances must be protected by

   i) a 3 amp fuse

   ii) a 13 amp fuse

   (Give at least three examples in each case.)

f) If you are using an appliance and the fuse 'blows', what two actions should you take before using the appliance again?

4 Lisa has just bought a hair dryer. The diagram shows some of the parts inside it.

a) Explain why:

i) the case is made of plastic and not metal

ii) the heating elements are *not* made of carbon

b) The hair dryer has a label with the following information:

Power rating	720 W
Supply	240 V a.c.

i) A power of one watt means that one joule of energy is transferred each second. How much energy is transferred by the hair dryer each second?

ii) What is the current supplied to the hair dryer.

$$\left(\text{Formula: current} = \frac{\text{power}}{\text{voltage}}. \right)$$

c) Suggest why the hair dryer must not be used by someone having a bath.

d) The safety cut-out is a *bimetallic strip*. Explain how this device operates.

5.4.4 Magnetism

1

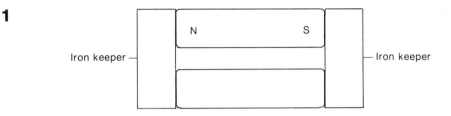

a) Bar magnets are frequently stored in pairs using iron 'keepers' as shown.

   i) Why is this done?

   ii) Copy the diagram and complete it to show how the poles of the lower magnet should be arranged.

b) The iron rods become induced magnets when placed as shown in the diagram below. Copy the diagram, and add labels to show the magnetic polarity (N or S) of the ends of both rods.

2 The bar magnet shown below is cut into two equal lengths, and each of these is divided again so that there are four pieces. Copy the diagram and add labels to show the magnetic poles (N or S) of each of the six smaller magnets.

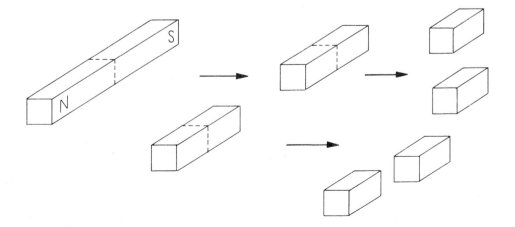

5.4.5 **Electromagnetic Effects**

1

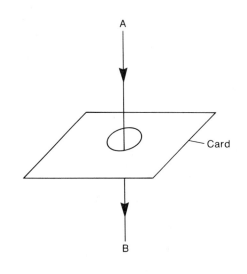

a) An electric current is flowing through the wire AB. Some iron filings are sprinkled on the card, which is then tapped gently. Draw the diagram showing the pattern you would expect to see in the iron filings.

b) Name a metal which would not show this pattern when its filings are placed on the card.

2 When a current is passed through the coil, the compass needle at point X points in the direction shown. The direction of magnetic north is as indicated.

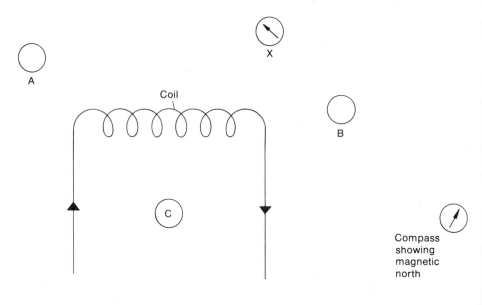

a) Copy the diagram and draw in the direction of the compass needles at positions A, B and C, when a current is flowing through the coil.

b) Indicate on your diagram the new direction of the compass needle at position A when the current is switched off.

c) Add labels N and S to your diagram to show the magnetic polarity of each end of the coil.

3 a) Copy the diagram of an electromagnet. Replace the letters A–D with correct labels chosen from the list below.

cell   soft iron core   solenoid   magnetic field lines

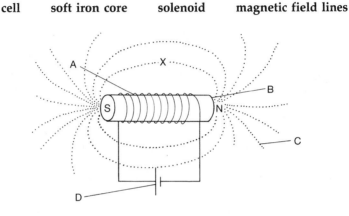

b) Add a compass to your diagram at point X, showing the direction in which the needle would point.

c) Give three ways of increasing the magnetic field strength of the electromagnet.

d) Describe one industrial use of electromagnets.

4

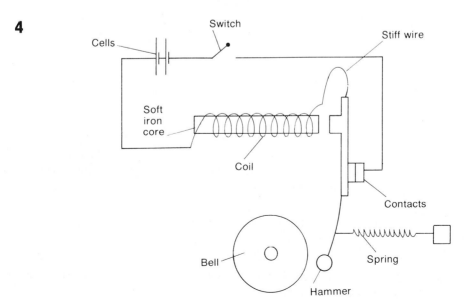

The diagram shows an electric bell. When the switch is closed, the hammer strikes the bell repeatedly.

a) Explain why the hammer strikes the bell when the switch is closed.

b) What is the purpose of the spring?

c) Explain why a soft iron core is used.

5 A lift in a tall building needs a very powerful electric motor to move it. The diagram below shows an arrangement which is used to switch the electric motor on and off.

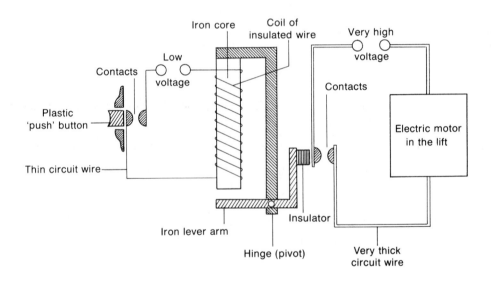

a) Name *one* substance which would be suitable for the circuit wire.

b) What can you see in the diagram that shows the electric motor is switched *off*? Explain your answer.

c) Carefully explain how an electric current flowing through the coil of insulated wire causes the electric motor to switch on.

d) Explain why this method of switching the motor on is safer than a single simple switch in the electric motor circuit.

6 The diagram below shows the main parts of a meter designed to measure electric current. there are two iron bars inside a coil. one bar is fixed and the other is on the end of a pivoted pointer.

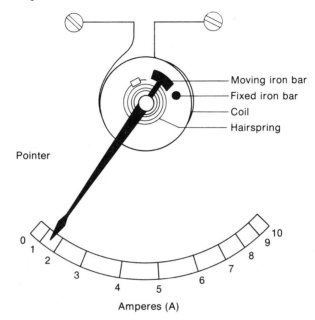

Moving iron bar
Fixed iron bar
Coil
Hairspring
Pointer
Amperes (A)

a)   i) Apart from heat, what will be produced inside the coil when electricity passes through it?

     ii) Explain what effects this will have on the two iron bars.

b)   What does the hairspring do?

7 The diagram below shows the flow of current in a wire coil placed in a magnetic field.

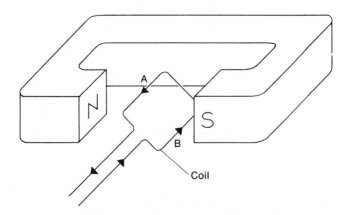

Coil

a)   What will happen to the coil in this situation, and why?

b)   Give *two* ways of increasing the magnitude of the force on the coil.

8

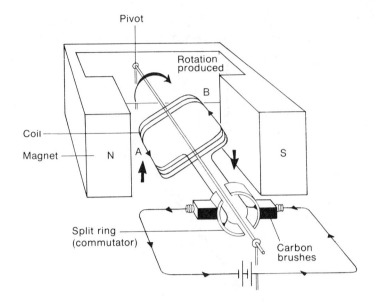

The d.c. motor shown above has a continuously rotating coil, as the split ring commutator reverses the direction of the current in the coil every half turn. The force on each of the coil segments A and B changes direction from one side of the magnet to the other.

a) Give *two* reasons why graphite (carbon) is a good choice of material for the brushes.

b) The motion of this device is jerky and it produces a small turning effect.

How would each of the following modifications improve the motor's performance? Copy and complete the table below to show how the modifications listed would improve the motor's performance.

Modification	Improvement produced
Several coils are used Each coil has many tens of turns The pole pieces are curved	

c) If the cell in the diagram was replaced by a sensitive, centre-zero ammeter, and the coil rotated by hand, what would the meter show when the coil began to rotate?

9 A sensitive, centre-zero ammeter (galvanometer) is connected into a closed loop of wire as shown in the diagram opposite. One section (XY) of the coil is then placed between the poles of a permanent magnet.

a) Copy the diagram.

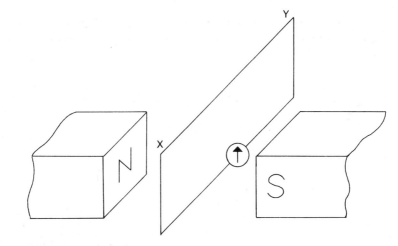

b) Copy and complete the following sentences.

   i) When the wire is stationary between the magnets, the meter reading is

       _____.

   ii) As the wire is moved upwards between the magnets, the meter needle
       shows a _____.

   iii) An _____ is induced in the wire when it is moving in the magnetic

        _____.

10

Sensitive centre-zero ammeter
(galvanometer)

When the permanent magnet is moved into the coil as shown, the galvanometer
kicks to the right. What would you expect to see on the galvanometer in the
following situations?

a) While removing the magnet from the coil to its starting position.

b) The magnet is turned round and the south pole is inserted into the coil.

c) The north pole of a stronger magnet is inserted as shown.

d) The magnet is stationary inside the coil.

11   Two coils are placed close together as shown. One has a soft iron core, and is part of an electromagnet. The other is connected to a sensitive centre-zero ammeter (galvanometer).

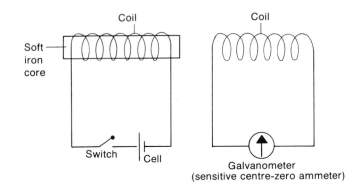

a)   Copy the diagram and draw in the magnetic field lines of the electromagnet.

b)   What will the galvanometer show as

   i) the electromagnet is switched on?

   ii) the electromagnet is switched off?

c)   Will the meter show a deflection after the electromagnet has been switched on for some time? Explain your answer.

d)   What would you expect to see happen in this experiment if the cell was replaced by an a.c. supply and the switch was closed?

12   The diagram below shows two C-cores in contact. Two coils, each of 120 turns, are placed around the cores. One coil is connected to a 4 V a.c. power supply, the other to a 6 V bulb.

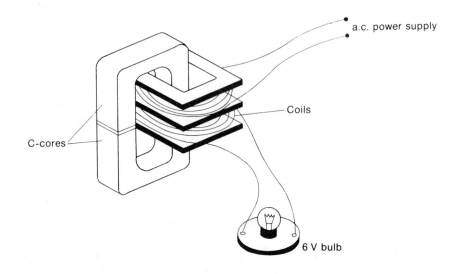

a)   i) When the a.c. power supply is switched on, what would happen to the bulb?

    ii) Would the same result be obtained using a 4 V d.c. power supply? Explain your answer.

b)   What change would you expect to see if the coil connected to the bulb had 180 turns?

c)   At the end of the experiment the C-cores were warmer than at the start. Why is this?

13   The diagram below shows a step-up transformer.

Input 12 V

Output

Primary
20 turns

Secondary
400 turns

a)   Would you expect the current flowing in the coils to be a.c. or d.c.?

b)   What is the output voltage?

c)   i) Give *two* reasons why a transformer such as this will not be 100% efficient.

    ii) How are modern transformers constructed to reduce the losses?

d)   Draw the standard symbol for a transformer using this example.

14   The diagram shows a simple dynamo.

a) i) Copy the diagram and add the following labels: Permanent magnet 1, Permanent magnet 2, Bulb, Coil, Brushes, Slip rings.

ii) Using this diagram explain very briefly how the dynamo produces a current which makes the bulb light up.

b) A dynamo changes energy from one form to another. Copy and complete the diagram to show the main energy changes connected with a dynamo.

_____ energy ⟶ Dynamo ⟶ _____ energy

5.4.6 Cathode Rays

1

Some of the following statements about cathode rays are true, some are false. Copy out each one, correcting those that are wrong.

a) Cathode rays are emitted from a heated negative electrode.

b) Cathode rays are not affected by magnetic fields.

c) Cathode rays can pass through a thick metal plate.

d) A cathode ray is a beam of electrons.

e) Cathode rays are attracted to a negatively charged plate.

f) Oscilloscopes and televisions make use of cathode rays.

2 A 50 Hz a.c. supply is connected across the Y-input terminals of an oscilloscope, and the time base adjusted to give the trace shown below.

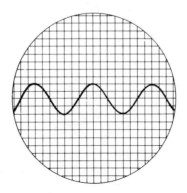

Draw the new appearance of the trace after the following changes have been made:

a) The frequency of the input is changed to 100 Hz.

b) The peak-to-peak voltage is halved.

c) The time base is switched off.

3 This question concerns the use of an oscilloscope as a voltmeter. The two traces below were obtained with the Y-gain set at 2 V/division.

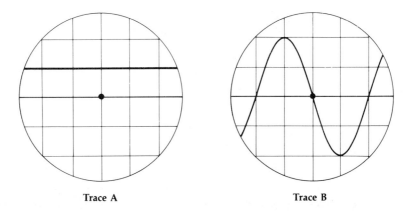

Trace A   Trace B

a)   i) What type of voltage has been connected across the Y input to produce trace A?

   ii) What type of voltage has been connected across the Y input to produce trace B?

b) What is the reading shown by trace A?

c) What is the amplitude of the voltage indicated by trace B?

d) Draw the appearance of the screen for trace A after the time base has been switched off.

e) Which of the traces, A or B, could have been produced in each of the following experiments?

Experiment 1   Experiment 2

4

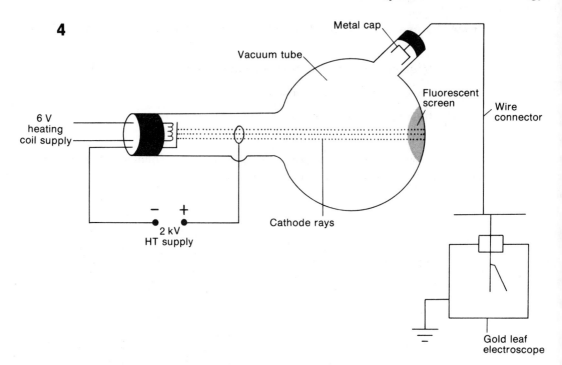

The apparatus above was used to demonstrate that cathode rays carry negative charge. The beam was deflected so that it hit the metal cap, which was connected to the plate of a gold leaf electroscope. The electroscope had been charged previously so that it carried a small negative charge, giving a small deflection of the leaf.

a)   Describe briefly how a negative charge can be induced in an electroscope.

b)   Why is the tube evacuated?

c)   How could the beam be deflected so that it hits the metal cap?

d)   If the cathode rays carry negative charge, what would you expect to see inside the electroscope when the cathode rays hit the metal cap?

e)   Apart from carrying negative charge, list *three* properties of cathode rays.

5   The diagram opposite shows some components of a black and white television tube.

a)   What is the function of the following items?

   i)   the heater

   ii)   the cathode

   iii)   the anode

   iv)   the coils

   v)   the coating on the screen

b)   The variable voltage on the modulator controls the number of electrons travelling towards the screen. What effect will this have on the appearance of the spot seen on the screen?

c) How does a colour television tube produce pictures which can show every
    colour of the spectrum?

6

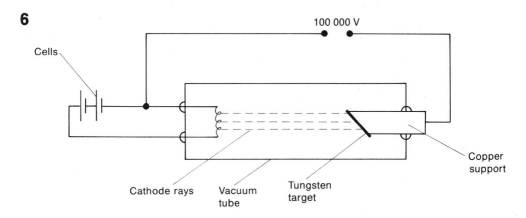

Which of the following are produced when cathode rays collide with the metal target
in the apparatus shown above?

A. neutrons

B. alpha particles

C. x-rays

D. sound waves

E. protons

5.5 USING LIGHT AND ELECTROMAGNETIC RADIATION

5.5.1 Shadows and Mirrors

1 Copy and complete these sentences about light, choosing words from this list to fill in the blanks:

> **energy   illuminated   luminous   reflect   straight wavelength**

a) Light is a form of _____.

b) Light is a wave motion with a _____ of about 0.0005 mm.

c) Objects that produce their own light are called _____ sources.

d) Other objects are _____ by this light and _____ it into our eyes.

e) Light travels in _____ lines.

2

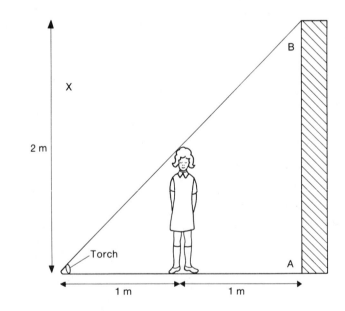

A child, one metre in height, is standing one metre away from a torch and one metre in front of a wall, as shown in the diagram.

a) How tall is her shadow?

b) If a second torch is shone from the position marked 'X', 1.5 metres above the ground, what would happen to the darkness of the shadow at

   i) point A?

   ii) point B?

c) Why is the shadow of a person standing under a street lamp not sharp?

d) Why is it better to have classrooms lit by long fluorescent lamps than single small lamps?

3 a) Copy the diagram below which shows a ray being reflected by a plane mirror.

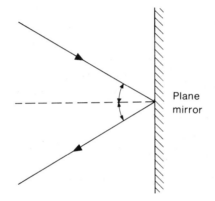

Plane mirror

b)   i) Add labels to your diagram for the following:
     Incident ray
     Reflected ray
     The normal

  ii) What is the relationship between these three?

c)   i) Add labels to your diagram for the following:
     Angle of incidence
     Angle of reflection

  ii) What is the relationship between these two?

4 a) List *three* ways to describe the image of a plane mirror.

b) **POLICE**

If you see this in the rear view mirror of your car, what is actually written on the front of the police car?

c) Show how two plane mirrors can be used to produce a periscope.

5 a)   Copy diagrams A and B and complete them to show how the parallel rays of light
are reflected by the two mirrors.

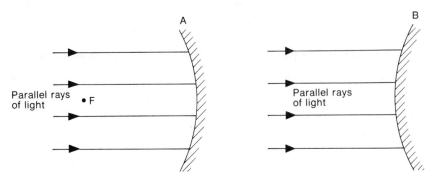

b)   Copy these sentences choosing only the correct alternatives from inside the
brackets.

i)   A mirror that curves in is called a (concave/convex) mirror and is a
(diverging/converging) mirror. Mirror A is (concave/convex).

ii) A mirror that curves outwards is a (concave/convex) mirror and is a
(diverging/converging mirror). Mirror B is (concave/convex).

c)   Mark on each of your diagrams A and B

i)   the focal length

ii) the centre of curvature

d)   Which type of mirror would be used as a driving mirror? Explain your
answer.

5.5.2 Refraction and Lenses

1   Match the words in the left-hand column with the definitions in the right-hand
column.

Words	Definitions
Refraction	Light rays 'bouncing back' from a surface.
Dispersion	The bending of light when it passes from one optical medium to another.
Reflection	The splitting up of white light into the colours of the rainbow.

2 a) Copy these sentences choosing only the correct alternatives from inside the brackets.

   i) Rays of light travelling from air into glass are bent or refracted (towards/ away from) the normal. This is because air is optically (less/more) dense than glass.

   ii) Rays of light travelling from glass into air are bent or refracted (towards/ away from) the normal.

   b) Copy and complete the following diagrams to show the approximate direction of the refracted rays.

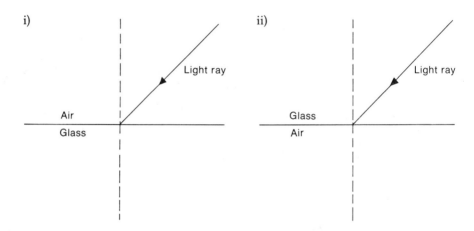

3 a) Copy the diagram below.

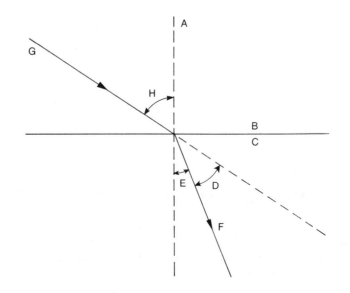

b) Copy the following list of terms and say which letter on the diagram belongs to which term.

> **Optically less dense medium**
> **Optically more dense medium**
> **Incident ray**
> **Refracted ray**
> **Normal**
> **Angle of incidence**
> **Angle of refraction**
> **Angle of deviation**

4   The refractive index of glass is 1.5, showing that the speed of light in a vacuum is 1.5 times greater than the speed of light in glass.

$$\text{refractive index of glass} \; = \; \frac{\text{speed of light in a vacuum}}{\text{speed of light in glass}}$$

$$= \; \frac{300\;000\;\text{km/s}}{200\;000\;\text{km/s}}$$

$$= \; 1.5$$

The diagram shows how a ray of light behaves on passing from a vacuum into a block of glass.

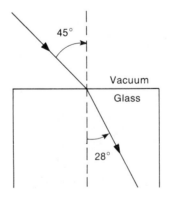

a)   Calculate $\dfrac{\sin 45^{\circ}}{\sin 28^{\circ}}$ using a pocket scientific calculator, and comment on the result.

b)   Draw diagrams showing what would happen to a ray of light on entering a vacuum from a block of glass as shown opposite. Find any unknown angles by calculation.

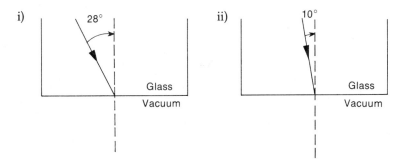

c) The refractive index of water is 1.33. Calculate the speed of light in water. (Speed of light in a vacuum = 300 000 km/s.)

5 a) Copy and complete the ray diagram to show how a swimming pool appears shallower than it really is, owing to refraction of light at the surface.

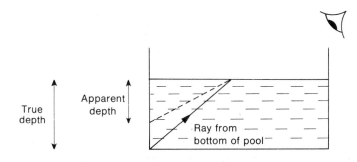

b) Explain how a rod appears to bend when partly immersed in water. You may wish to copy and amend the following diagram to help explain your answer.

c) A coin is placed on the bottom of a plastic cup. An observer stands above and to one side of the cup so that the coin is just hidden behind the rim. Draw a diagram showing this, and which also explains how the coin becomes visible when the cup is carefully filled with water, even though the observer does not move.

6 A swimming pool appears to be 1.5 m deep. If the refractive index of water is 1.33, what is the real depth? Show your working.

7

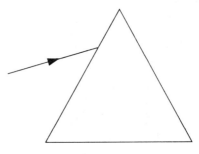

a) Copy and complete the diagram above to show how the prism **refracts** and **disperses** light.

b) Copy and complete the diagram below to show how internal reflection occurs in a prism.

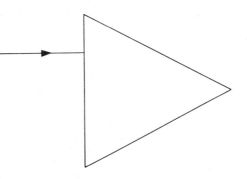

c) i) Explain how two prisms can be used to make a periscope.

ii) Why is it better to use prisms than plane mirrors?

8 a) Copy diagrams A and B and complete them to show how the parallel rays emerge from each lens.

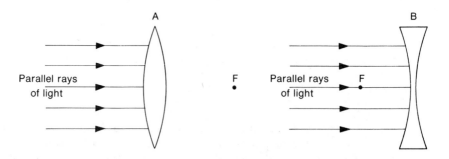

b) Copy these sentences choosing only the correct alternatives from inside the brackets.

i) A lens which is thicker at the centre than at the end is called a (concave/ convex) lens and is a (converging/diverging) lens. Lens A is a (concave/ convex) lens.

   ii) A lens which is thinner at its centre is called a (concave/convex) lens and is a (converging/diverging lens). Lens B is a (concave/convex) lens.

c) Mark on your diagrams the **focal length** of each lens.

9 The power of a lens is measured in dioptres (D):

$$\text{power of lens (D)} = \frac{1}{\text{focal length (m)}}$$

The power of a convex lens is positive, while that of a concave lens is negative.

a) What is the focal length of a lens?

b) Calculate the focal length, in centimetres, of lenses with the following powers.
   i) $+0.5$ D
   ii) $+20.0$ D
   iii) -1.5 D

c) Which of the lenses in part b) could be used as a magnifying glass?

5.5.3 The Eye

1

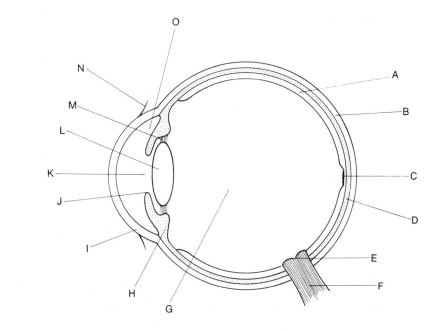

Make a large copy of the previous diagram of the eye and replace the letters A–O with the correct label chosen from the following list:

aqueous humour   blind spot   choroid   ciliary body
conjunctiva   cornea   iris   lens   ligaments
optic nerve   pupil   retina   sclera   vitreous humour
yellow spot

2   Match the following words and phrases to make correct sentences about the eye and seeing. Each sentence should begin with one of the phrases on the left and finish with one on the right. The first one has been done for you as an example:

The iris consists of . . . circular and radial muscles.

a)   **The iris consists of**   shape.

b)   **The retina contains**   messages to the brain.

c)   **The choroid contains**   dim light.

d)   **The yellow spot contains**   bright light.

e)   **The blind spot has**   circular and radial muscles.

f)   **The ligaments hold**   millions of light sensitive cells.

g)   **The pupil allows**   many blood vessels.

h)   **The cornea bends (or refracts) the** only cones.

i)   **The lens can change**   no light-sensitive cells

j)   **The optic nerve sends**   the lens.

k)   **The rods respond to**   light to enter the eye.

l)   **The cones respond to**   light rays.

3   a)   Copy the diagram and complete it to show how an image of the spider is formed on the retina.

b)   Why do we not see everything upside down?

4 a) Most of the refraction of light takes place at the front surface of the cornea. The lens acts as an adjustment device to focus light coming from different distances. The diagram below shows how the lens changes shape. Study the diagram, then copy and complete the table.

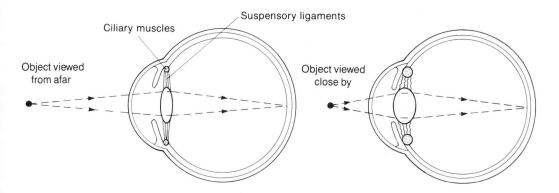

	Is the lens round or flat?	Are the ciliary muscles relaxed or contracted?	Are the ligaments slack or tight?	Are the light rays bent a lot or a little?
When looking at near objects When looking at far away objects				

b) Copy the sentence below choosing only the correct alternative, A, B, C or D, to complete it:

The ability of the lens to change shape in order to focus light coming from different distances is called

A. adjustment

B. accommodation

C. refraction

D. suspension

c) Write an account of how the eye focuses light. (Use the information in this question.)

d) Explain why people usually need reading glasses by the time they are fifty, even if they have had excellent eyesight until then.

5 a) Copy the passage below and fill in the gaps with words from the following list. Some words may be used more than once.

> radial   larger   smaller   circular   relax (es)
> contract (s)   less   retina

In bright light the pupil becomes _____, owing to the action of the iris. The iris consists of _____ and _____ muscles. When one _____ the other _____. In bright light, the _____ muscles relax and the _____muscles _____; thus the pupil becomes _____, allowing _____ light to fall on the _____ at the back of the eye.

b) Copy the diagrams of the iris below. Replace the letters A–F with labels chosen from this list:

wide pupil in dim light
narrow pupil in bright light
circular muscles contracted
circular muscles relaxed
radial muscles contracted
radial muscles relaxed

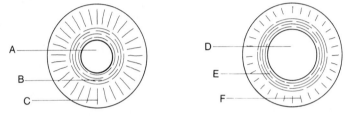

6 The diagrams illustrate two problems of sight, short sight (A) in which distant objects appear blurred, and long sight (B), in which near objects appear blurred.

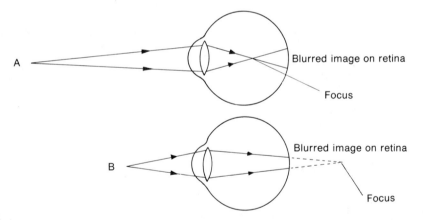

a) What type of lens, convex or concave, should be used in spectacles to correct

    i) short sight?

    ii) long sight?

b) Use diagrams to show how a suitable lens can correct each of the defects shown.

c) Which of the two defects described would most likely occur in a person with an unusually long eyeball (measured from cornea to retina)?

7 Write a short essay entitled 'Two Eyes are Better than One'.

5.5.4 Optical Devices

1 Which of the optical components listed would be suitable for the following applications? A different component is required for each application.

> **convex lens**   **convex mirror**   **concave mirror**   **parabolic mirror**
> **concave lens**   **plane mirror**

a) a shaving mirror

b) a telescope mirror

c) a wide-field security mirror in a shop

d) a magnifying glass

e) a correcting lens for short-sight

f) a periscope

2 The pin-hole camera (below) can be used to take photographs without using a lens.

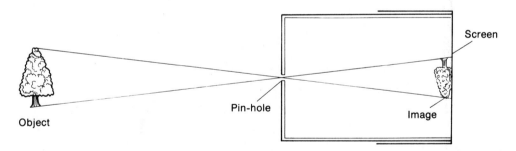

a) Copy and complete the following sentence by choosing the correct word from the brackets.

The image formed by a pin-hole camera is (real/virtual) and upright/inverted).

b) Describe *two* ways of making the image bigger.

c) State *two* effects on the image of making the pin-hole larger.

d) Why are pin-hole cameras rarely used to take photographs?

e) During a partial eclipse of the Sun, small images of the 'crescent' of the partially eclipsed Sun can be seen in the shadow beneath a leafly tree. Explain this observation.

3 The diagram shows a screen with a lens in front of it. In front of the lens is a flower.

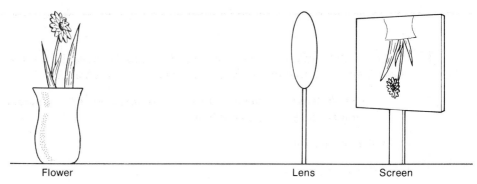

Flower   Lens   Screen

a) The image of the flower on the screen is fuzzy. Suggest *two* ways in which you could make the image sharp.

b) Once the image is sharp, the flower is moved a little way towards the lens. What must you now do with the screen to make the image sharp again?

c) What difference would you see in the image if the lens was replaced by another of the same power, but with only half its diameter?

d) With the help of a diagram, explain how the lens could be used together with a lightproof box and photographic film to make a simple camera.

4

The above diagram shows the arrangement of lenses in a telescope. This type is known as a refractor.

a) Which of the two lenses has the longer focal length?

b) Is the image formed by the eye lens real or virtual?

c) How is the telescope focused?

d) How could the final image be made upright?

e) Why are the final images in **astronomical telescopes** inverted and not corrected as in part e)?

f) Which of the following features of the telescope determines the faintest object the telescope will reveal?

A. Focal length of the objective lens.

B. Focal length of the eye lens.

C. Diameter of the objective lens.

D. Diameter of the eye lens.

g) What is used to gather light in a reflecting telescope?

5 The diagram shows how a single convex lens can be used as a magnifying glass.

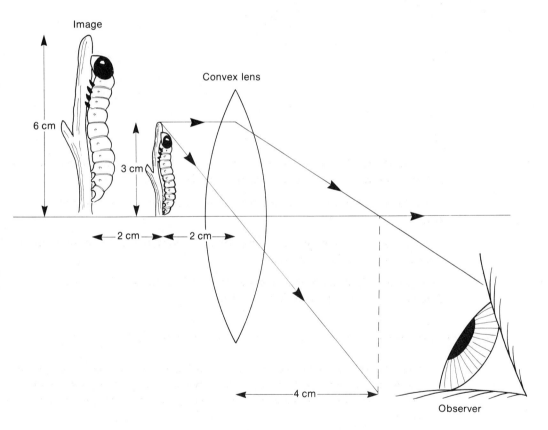

a) What is the focal length of the lens?

b) On a copy of the diagram, extend the rays backwards to show how the eye sees an enlarged image of the object.

c) Would it be possible to obtain an image of the enlarged view on a piece of white card? Explain your answer.

d) What magnification has been given in this experiment?

6   The diagram shows two solid glass rods, similar to optical fibres. Both are of the same type of glass and are surrounded by air.

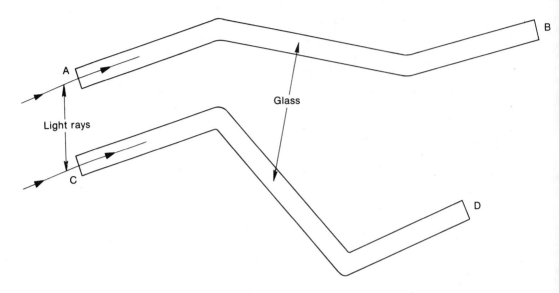

a)   It is found that the ray of light entering the rod at A reaches B, but the ray entering the rod at C does not reach D. Explain why.

b)   Copy the first diagram and complete it by showing how the light ray travels from A to B.

c)   Light takes 10^{-3} s to travel 2×10^5 m along an optical fibre. Use these figures to calculate the speed of the light in glass.

d)   The speed of light in a vacuum is 3×10^8 m/s. Explain any difference between this value and the speed of light in glass.

7   Read the passage below and answer the questions which follow.

Optical fibres are used in medicine. Mounted in a device called an endoscope they can be used to examine the inside of the alimentary canal. A bronchoscope can be used to examine the respiratory passages and lungs. The diagram opposite shows an endoscope.

In the coherent bundle, optical fibres are arranged so that they have exactly the same positions at both ends of the bundle allowing an image to be transmitted. The ends of the bundle are evenly cut and polished and each fibre carries a small part of the image. In the incoherent bundle the fibres are arranged randomly. This allows light to be sent down the tube but no image can be seen.

The endoscope will also include a channel which allows water to be passed down to clean the lens. Other channels may also be present, for example one which allows biopsy probes to be put into the body. These are used to remove small samples of tissue for testing.

The end of the endoscope tube is flexible and can be moved around inside the body. There is no heat produced at the tip, since the source of light is at the other end.

a) Name *two* medical instruments which involve the use of optical fibres and say what they are used for.

b) How are the optical fibres arranged in
   i) a coherent bundle?
   ii) an incoherent bundle?

c) Why are both types of fibre bundle used in these medical instruments?

c) Why is it important to keep the lens clean?

e) Suggest one medical condition which may be diagnosed using an endoscope.

f) What is the advantage of
   i) the end of the tube being flexible?
   ii) no heat being produced at the tip?

g) What is a biopsy?

h) Briefly describe one other, non-medical, use of optical fibres.

5.5.5 **Electromagnetic Radiation**

1 a) Copy the diagram below, which shows how a prism produces a continuous
       (rainbow) spectrum from white light, and add the missing colours.

```
                                                    Yellow
                                                    Green
```

   b) Which colour of the rainbow corresponds to light with the longest wavelength?

   c) The diagram shows how a rainbow is formed by raindrops.

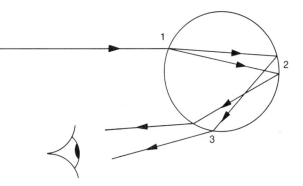

   i) Will the rainbow be visible looking towards or away from the Sun?

   ii) As shown, will the rainbow have red or violet at the top?

   iii) At which of the points 1, 2 and 3 does **refraction** occur?

   iv) At which of the points 1, 2 and 3 does **reflection** occur?

2 A thermometer with its bulb painted black is placed just beyond the red region of the
    continuous (rainbow) spectrum produced from sunlight using a prism.

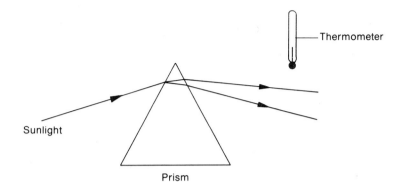

Sunlight

Prism

What would happen to the reading on the thermometer, and why?

3 Three projectors are pointed at a white screen. The projectors are equally bright. One has a red filter attached, the second has a green filter and the third a blue filter. A student looks at the screen. The colours he sees are shown in the diagram.

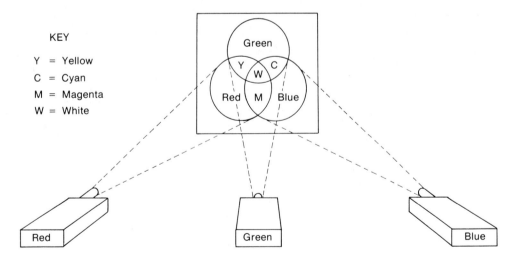

KEY

Y = Yellow
C = Cyan
M = Magenta
W = White

a)   i) Name two **secondary** colours.

ii) Name two **complementary** colours.

b) Use the results from this experiment to predict the colour seen on the screen in the following examples. The filters used are shown.

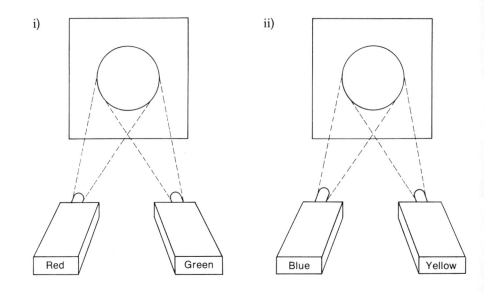

i)   ii)

4   Some dyes used to stain biological specimens for microscopic examination are fluorescent. They absorb ultraviolet light and emit visible light. The diagram represents a ray of ultraviolet radiation. (1 nm = 0.000 000 001 m)

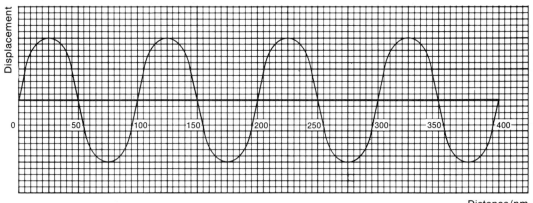

Distance/nm

a)   What is the wavelength, in nm, of this radiation?

The diagram below represents the visible spectrum.

b)   The ultraviolet light in part a) was absorbed by a dye and visible light was emitted. If the wavelength of the emitted radiation had increased by a factor of 5 estimate the colour of the light produced.

c) An object appears yellow when viewed under white light. It appears red when viewed under red light and it appears black when viewed under blue light. Explain why.

5 a) Place the following regions of the electromagnetic spectrum in order of increasing wavelength.

ultraviolet	**radio waves**	**visible light**	**X-rays**
infra-red	**gamma rays**		

b) Correctly match each region of the spectrum with an application.

Region of spectrum	*Application*
Visible light	Sun beds and sun lamps
Radio waves	Sterilising pre-packed hospital equipment
X-rays	Finding people buried in collapsed buildings
Gamma rays	Communication over long distances
Ultraviolet	Laser surgery
Infra-red	Diagnosing broken bones

6 a) Explain what is meant by saying that the waves from a source are **plane-polarised**.

b) The TV aerials on the houses in a street are arranged as shown in the diagram.

i) The aerials all point in the same direction. What are they pointing to?

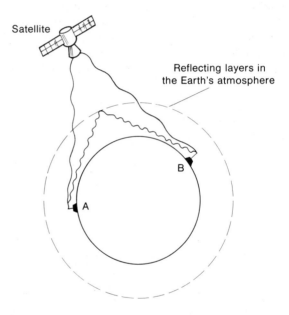

ii) Explain why the aerials are **all** arranged so that their **dipoles** are in the same plane in each case.

7

ii) Explain why the aerials are **all** arranged so that their **dipoles** are in the same plane in each case.

Communication between stations at points A and B on the Earth's surface can take place using short wave radio signals (wavelength 10–100 m, frequency 3–30 MHz) or a via a satellite link using microwaves (wavelength 0.1–0.01 m, frequency 3–30 GHz).

$(1 \text{ MHz} = 10^6 \text{ Hz}, \ 1 \text{ GHz} = 10^9 \text{ Hz})$

a) What prevents the use of microwaves for long-distance communication on the Earth's surface?

b) Why are microwaves needed for communication via satellite?

c) List *two* advantages of microwave links which arise through the high frequency of the radiation used.

d) Describe *one* application of microwaves in the home, and any hazards associated with their use.

TOPIC 6

Information Technology, Electronics and Microelectronics

6.1.1 Components and Applications

1 A resistor has four coloured bands as shown in the diagram.

1st band   2nd band   3rd band   4th band

a) What information is obtained from the first two bands?

b) What does the third band signify?

c) The fourth band is usually silver or gold. Explain what each of these colours indicates.

d) What is the value of each of the following resistors? Consult a copy of the colour code for resistors if you cannot remember it.

	First band	Second band	Third band	Fourth band
i)	red	red	black	silver
ii)	orange	white	brown	gold
iii)	brown	black	red	gold
iv)	orange	white	orange	gold
v)	red	violet	yellow	gold

e) What are the minimum and maximum values of the resistor in d) part v)?

2 Circuit diagrams often give resistor values in the BS 1852 code. What are the values of the following resistors, expressed in their code?

a) 6K8M

b) R47K

c) 5R6J

3 a) Miniaturisation has allowed entire circuits to be constructed on a wafer of silicon small enough to pass through the eye of a needle. Other than resistors, what *three* fundamental components would you expect to find on such a circuit?

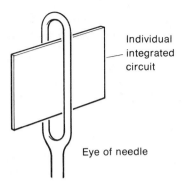

b) Moore's law, formulated in 1960, states that the number of components that would be integrated on a single chip would double every year. If in 1970 a chip could hold 100 components, and assuming Moore's law is valid, calculate the number of components which will be integrated on a single silicon chip in the year 2000.

4 a) i) What does the direction of the arrow in the symbol for a diode indicate?

ii) In which of the following circuits will the bulb light up when the switch is closed?

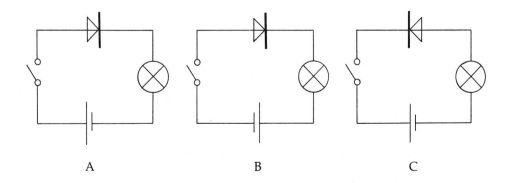

A B C

b) Describe *one* application of the diode in electronics.

5 Copy and complete the following table, which lists the symbols of common components together with their name.

Symbol   *Name of component*

6 The graph shows how the current flowing through a semiconductor diode changes as the voltage across its ends increases.

a) i) At what applied voltage does the diode begin to conduct significantly?

ii) What is the current flowing through the diode at an applied voltage of 0.8 V?

b) Describe the behaviour of the diode.

c) i) Sketch the graph of current against voltage that you would expect to obtain if the connections to the diode were interchanged.

ii) Sketch another graph to show the behaviour of an *ideal* diode.

7 The circuit shown below is used on a bicycle which has both batteries and a dynamo to power the lights. The diodes conduct only when the applied voltage exceeds 0.5 V.

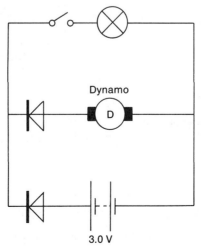

a)   Give one advantage and one disadvantage of using a dynamo in place of batteries.

b)   Explain how this circuit prolongs the life of the batteries.

8   Four diodes are arranged in a bridge circuit as shown below. Oscilloscopes are connected across the input and output terminals.

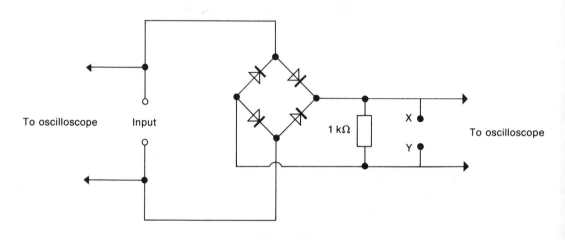

a)   The trace on the screen of the input oscilloscope is shown below. Draw a similar diagram showing the trace you would expect to see on the screen of the output oscilloscope, which has identical gain and time base settings.

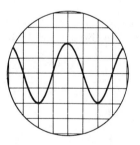

b)   A smoothing capacitor is connected between the contacts X and Y. Sketch the trace which would be seen on the screen of the output oscilloscope.

9   a)   Which of the following elements can be used to make transistors?

silicon   iron   boron   germanium   carbon

b) Copy the transistor symbols shown below and add the labels **base, collector** and **emitter** to the correct terminals.

npn transistor   pnp transistor

10 X is a probe which can be connected to contact A or B. Copy the circuit diagram and explain how it can be used to demonstrate the use of a transistor as a switch.

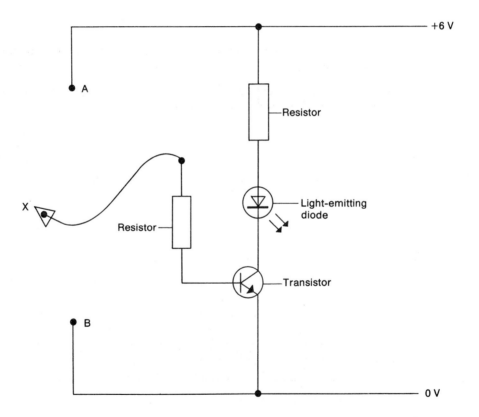

11 The circuit drawn on the next page can be used as a rain detector. When it rains, water falls on the sensor and the bulb lights up.

a) Draw a diagram of the circuit using the correct symbol for each of the components A–E.

b)   i) When soldering the transistor leads, Ann placed a crocodile clip on each, just below the transistor body. Why was this necessary?

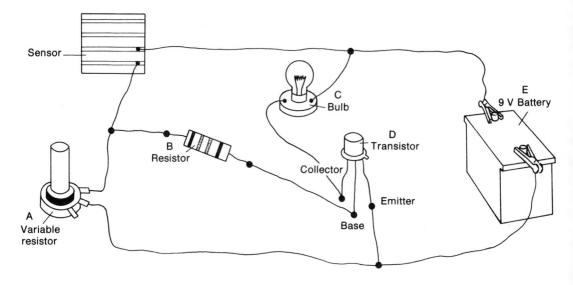

Sensor

C
Bulb

E
9 V Battery

D
Transistor

B
Resistor

Collector

Emitter

A
Variable
resistor

Base

ii) Explain why it is wrong to solder components into a circuit with the battery connected up.

c) Copy and complete the flow diagram to show which component in the circuit provides each stage in the alarm system.

DETECTOR:		SWITCH:		DISPLAY WARNING:
....		....		....

d) Write out the passage below, inserting the missing words.

The transistor in the circuit is biased using a _____ divider, which consists of a variable resistor together with the _____. When the _____ is dry, no current flows into the _____ of the transistor and the bulb is _____. When it is raining, the _____ becomes a conductor and now the current flowing into the _____ of the transistor causes a current to flow between the _____ and _____, and the bulb is _____. The transistor is acting as a _____.

e) Suggest one use for this circuit inside the home.

12 The circuit opposite can be used to switch on a bulb automatically in the dark.

a) On a copy of the circuit, label clearly the components which are acting as a potential divider.

b) Name components A and B.

c) What is the purpose of the variable resistor R_1?

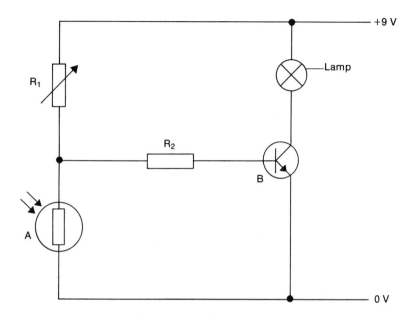

d) i) Describe how the circuit operates. Give your answer as a sequence of events.

ii) If the lamp is placed close to component A when the circuit is in a darkened room, the lamp will begin to flash on and off. This is due to a condition of **feedback**. Explain what is meant by feedback, and state (with reasons) whether this is an example of **positive** or **negative feedback**.

e) How would the operation of the circuit differ if the positions of resistor R_1 and component A were interchanged?

13 During wine making, the fermenting solution must be kept at a constant temperature for best results.

a) Draw a circuit, using the components listed below, that will sound an alarm if the solution becomes too cold.

D.C. power supply

Resistor

Variable resistor

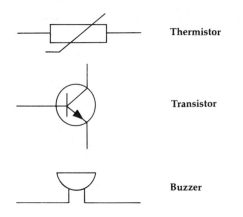

Thermistor

Transistor

Buzzer

b)   Explain how you would adjust the circuit so that the alarm sounds at a slightly lower temperature than before.

14   The diagram below shows an op amp used as an inverting amplifier

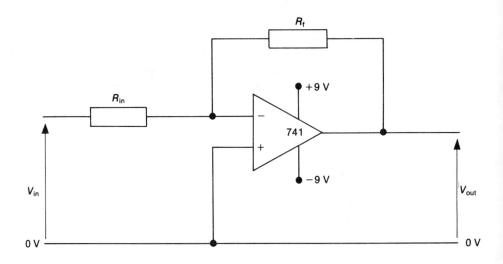

a)   i)   What happens to the output voltage (V_{out}) as the input voltage (V_{in}) becomes more positive?

ii)   In some situations it is possible for the output of the op amp to go into saturation. What is meant by saturation?

b)   What is the purpose of the resistor R_f?

c)   Calculate the voltage gain when $R_f = 10 \text{ k}\Omega$, $R_{in} = 2 \text{ k}\Omega$.

d)   What would V_{out} be if $R_f = 100 \text{ k}\Omega$, $R_{in} = 2 \text{ k}\Omega$ and $V_{in} = -1 \text{ V}$?

e) Copy and complete the following table by calculating the missing values.

V_{in}	R_{in}	R_f	V_{out}
+100 mV	10 kΩ	100 kΩ	
+10 mV		250 kΩ	−150 mV
−2.5 mV	10 kΩ		+2.5 V
	10 kΩ	1 MΩ	+7.5 V

15 The diagram shows a time delay circuit which includes an op amp.

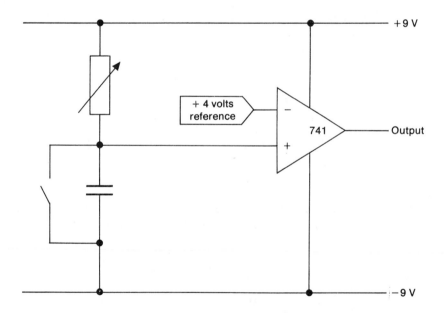

a) Describe, in simple terms, how the time delay circuit operates.

b) What would be the effect of an increase in the value of the capacitance on the length of the time delay?

c) What adjustment must be made to the variable resistor to increase the length of the time delay?

6.1.2 Switches and Relays

1 The diagram below shows a reed switch. When a permanent magnet is placed next to the capsule, the reeds attract and the switch closes.

Reed

Capsule filled
with nitrogen

a) Why is the capsule filled with nitrogen?

b) Will the reed switch close if a permanent magnet is placed next to it as shown in the diagram below? Explain your answer.

N

S

Permanent magnet

c) The diagram shows how a reed switch can be used as a safety device for a microwave oven. Explain how the device works.

Reed switch (actuates
microwave generator
power supply) set into
wall of microwave oven

N

S

Permanent magnet
inset in door edge

2   The diagram below shows a small mammal trap, which has its own d.c. power supply.

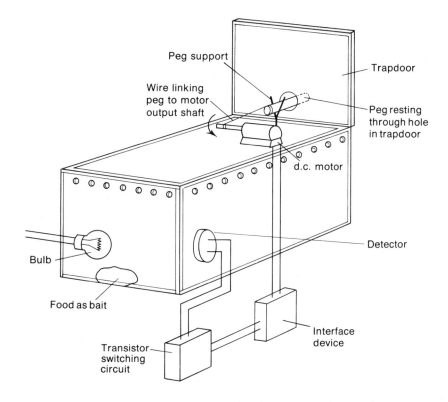

a)   Suggest a suitable material for making the container for the trap. Give reasons for your answer.

b)   Name a suitable detector for the trap.

c)   Name a suitable interface device.

d)   Devise a method of switching the motor off once the peg has been removed and the trapdoor has fallen. Explain how your method works.

3   The diagram on the next page shows a relay, operated by an electromagnet, which is used to switch on a motor.

a)   i) Explain why the core is made from soft iron.

       ii) Suggest a suitable material for the insulating anchorage.

b)   List the sequence of events which take place, from the moment the switch is closed, to the time when the motor starts.

c)   i) What is the advantage of switching on the motor using a relay in this way?

       ii) Suggest one practical application of this system.

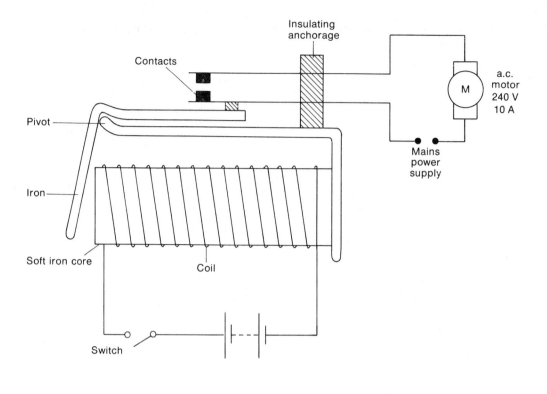

6.1.3 Logic Circuits

1 The diagram below shows a simple circuit involving a switch, cell and lamp. With 0 representing 'switch open' or 'lamp off', and 1 meaning 'switch closed' or 'lamp on', the two states of the circuit can be listed in table form:

Result table	
Switch A	*Lamp Z*
Open	Off
Closed	On

Truth table	
Input A	*Output Z*
0	0
1	1

Construct truth tables like the one above for the following circuits, each involving two switches. Make sure you cover all combinations.

a)

Inputs		Output
A	B	Z

Switch A   Switch B   Lamp Z

b)

Switch A

Lamp Z

Switch B

Inputs		Output
A	B	Z

2   a)   Match the following *types* of logic gate with the correct *symbol*.

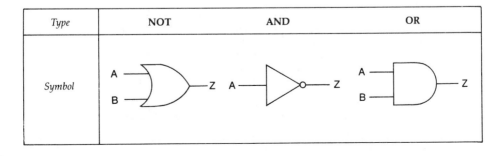

Type	NOT	AND	OR
Symbol	A, B → Z	A → Z	A, B → Z

b) Copy and complete the following truth tables for each named logic gate.

i) AND

Inputs		Output
A	B	Z
0	0	0
0	1	
1	0	
1	1	

ii) NAND

Inputs		Output
A	B	Z
0	0	
0	1	1
1	0	
1	1	0

iii) NOR

Inputs		Output
A	B	Z
0	0	
0	1	0
1	0	
1	1	0

3 a) In which type(s) of logic gate is

i) the output *on* (1) when both inputs are *on* (1)?
ii) the output *off* (0) when both inputs are *off* (0)?
iii) the output *on* (1) when only one of the inputs is *on* (1)?

b) Copy and complete the truth table for the combination of logic gates shown below.

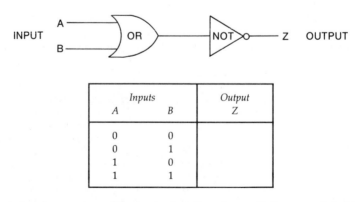

Inputs		Output
A	B	Z
0	0	
0	1	
1	0	
1	1	

c) Draw a simpler version of the logic circuit underneath the completed truth table.

4 A student designed a circuit for a fire alarm. It is shown in the diagram below.

a) Copy the circuit and label the components A–D. Select labels from the following list:

   switch   resistor   variable resistor   cell   thermistor
   lamp   diode   light-dependent resistor   light-emitting diode

b) Which logic gate (or gates) in the circuit is (are) responsible for the fact that:

   i) the alarm sounds when a settee is burning vigorously, but not when a light is turned on in the room?

   ii) the switch can be used to test the alarm in a cold, dark room?

c) Explain why this alarm might fail to sound when there is a fire. Assume that there is no electrical fault.

5 Draw a circuit diagram to show how you would use a suitable logic gate or combination of logic gates to switch on a greenhouse heater automatically when the temperature falls below a certain level at night. Underneath your circuit diagram, explain briefly how it works.

6　A chicken farmer breeds chickens all the year round. His hatching shed must be kept within a few degrees of the correct temperature. There are two methods of controlling the temperature – a cold air blower and a convector heater. Both are controlled by a computer which receives information from a temperature sensor in the shed. The computer is programmed to maintain the correct temperature by operating the blower and heater in response to data from the sensor. A flow diagram for the operating program is shown below.

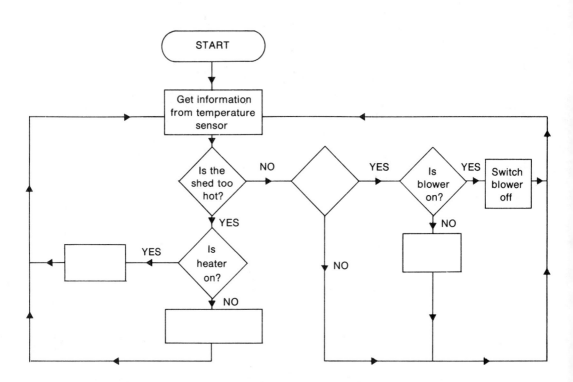

a)　Copy and complete the flow diagram.

b)　Name an electronic component which could be used to sense the temperature in the shed.

c)　This method of controlling the temperature depends on **feedback**. Explain what is meant by feedback.

d)　Give one advantage and one disadvantage of an automatic control system such as this.

6.1.4 Storing, Processing and Communicating Information

1 a) List four devices used to store information. For each, state the form in which the information is stored.

b) Describe the use in everyday life of any two devices which use microelectronic components.

2 a) Explain the difference between information in **analogue** form and **digital** form.

b) ii) Describe two situations where information received by a person is in digital form.

ii) Describe two situations where information received by a person is in analogue form.

c) State *one* advantage and *one* disadvantage of transmitting information in digital form.

d) The block diagram below shows the features of an information transmission system, such as that used to send a message from one computer to another.

i) Copy the diagram.

ii) Name *one* input device which can be used to put information into a micro-computer.

iii) Name *two* output devices which allow users to obtain information from a microcomputer.

3 To convert the continuous, analogue signal shown below to digital form, sample measurements must be taken at regular intervals. This must be done sufficiently frequently to give an accurate representation of the changing analogue signal. The analogue values are digitised by assigning a binary code to each. Once in digital form, the information can be processed, stored or transmitted as required.

a) i) Copy and complete the following table, which shows the conversion of the analogue signal to digital form.

Sample time	Signal decimal value	Binary signal value (8 bit)
1	5	00000101
2	10	00001010
3		
4		
5		
6		
7		
8		
9		
10		
11		
12		

ii) Is the sampling frequency adequate? Explain your answer.

b) Devise a method of converting the letters of your first name into 8 bit binary code.

4 a) Computers are widely used in hospitals as part of patient-monitoring systems, and to help with record keeping. For instance, heart rate can be monitored by a computer in a life-support system.

i) Suggest *two* other pieces of information about a patient's condition which could be monitored by computer.

      ii) Give *two* advantages which computers have over humans in life-support systems.

      iii) List *two* tasks which medical staff can perform better than a computer.

   b) Describe how information held on a computer could be used by a doctor to help diagnose an illness.

   c) What problems can arise from keeping hospital records on a computer?

   d) List *two* benefits arising from the computerisation of hospital records.

5 A **bistable** or 'flip-flop' is a logic circuit which is used to store the binary data in the central processing unit of computers. The following diagram shows a bistable, constructed by cross-coupling two NOR gates.

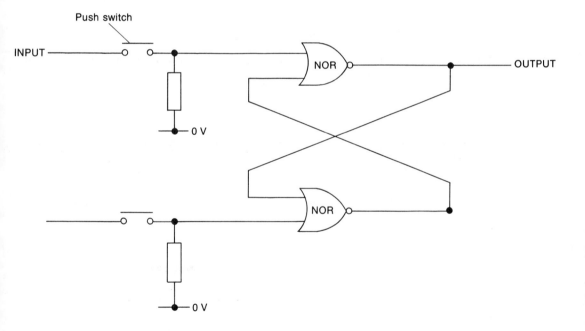

   a) What must happen to cause the bistable to revert to its original state following an input signal?

   b) It is said that the device 'remembers' that an input has been made. Explain what this means by describing the operation of the bistable. You should assume that the output is at logic 1 initially.

   c) i) What name is given to a bistable with only one of its outputs in use, like that shown in the diagram?

      ii) What term is used to describe a set of bistables linked together to store data?

6 Optical fibres, made of very pure glass, can be used in transmitting telephone calls as shown in the flow diagram below. More calls can be transmitted using these fibres than when conventional cables of a similar diameter are used.

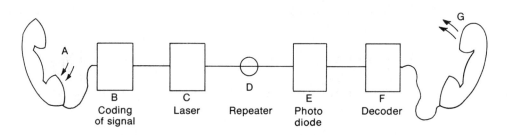

B
Coding
of signal

C
Laser

D

E
Photo
diode

F
Decoder

a) Briefly explain what is happening at each stage A–G.

b) Between which stages in the sequence is the information transmitted using optical fibres?

c) What is a repeater and why is it needed?

d) Why are telephone conversations transmitted using optical fibres more difficult to 'tap', and therefore more secure?

7 The diagram below shows a simple radio receiver built by a student. It incorporates a ZN414 radio integrated circuit.

Coil

The coil is made by wrapping 50 turns of thin copper wire around a small cardboard tube. A 10 cm ferrite rod is then placed inside the coil. The radio can be tuned by slowly pushing the rod in or out of the coil.

a) i) Copy the circuit diagram, and add the following labels at the correct positions. Some may need to be used more than once.

cell   integrated circuit   earphone   capacitor   resistor

ii) Suggest one operation carried out by the integrated circuit.

b) Given a list of radio programmes and the wavelength of each station, describe how you would investigate how the wavelength of the radio waves received depends on the length of rod inside the coil.

c) An alternative method of tuning the circuit involves replacing one of the capacitors by a **variable capacitor**. Indicate clearly on your diagram which capacitor should be replaced.

8 In approximately 750 words, discuss the impact which modern information technology has had on our lives. You should mention data storage systems, data processing and communication of information in your answer.

TOPIC 7

The Nature of Science

7.1.1 The History of Science

1   Our modern knowledge and understanding of science and medicine is a result of the work of many scientists over hundreds of years. As long ago as 500 BC the Greeks were making and explaining observations and they were well known for inventing things. Below is a list of some famous scientists.

Match each of the names with the short descriptions of their contribution to the advancement of science. (You may need to use reference books.)

	Scientist	*Advancement*
a)	Galileo Galilei 1564–1642	Discovered that air is composed of several gases, amongst them oxygen. Also that plants give out oxygen.
b)	Sir Isaac Newton 1642–1727	Developed the theory of relativity.
c)	Joseph Priestley 1733–1804	Discovered the element radium and worked on the new science radioactivity.
d)	John Dalton 1766–1844	Observed that all planets do not go round the Earth. Discovered the satellites of Jupiter.
e)	Dmitri Mendeleev 1834–1907	Discovered the electron, making possible the great developments in electronics in the twentieth century.
f)	Marie Curie 1864–1934	Split the atom and discovered that the atom is made up of a nucleus surrounded by a cloud of electrons.
g)	Sir Joseph Thomson 1856–1940	Classified the chemical elements in a table upon which the modern classification system is based.
h)	Henrietta Leavitt 1868–1921	Discovered a connection between a variable star's period of pulsation and its true luminosity, enabling its distance to be calculated.
i)	Ernest Rutherford 1871–1937	Split white light into a spectrum. Formulated the laws of motion. Made the first reflecting telescope that worked well.
j)	Albert Einstein 1879–1955	Explained the laws of chemistry in terms of atoms and molecules. Represented the atoms of substances by symbols.

2 The scientists listed below have all made a contribution to the advancement of biological or medical knowledge. Use reference books to find out about them. Write a **brief** summary of the work of each one.

a) Anton van Leeuwenhoek 1632–1723

b) Robert Hooke 1635–1703

c) Edward Jenner 1749–1823

d) Charles Darwin 1809–1882

e) Robert Koch 1848–1910

f) Gregor Mendel 1822–1884

g) Louis Pasteur 1822–1895

h) Joseph Lister 1827–1912

i) Sir Alexander Fleming 1881–1955

j) Francis Crick 1916– and James Watson 1928–

3 Briefly describe the scientist(s) and events associated with any *five* of the following scientific advances.

a) The understanding that objects fall to the ground owing to a force we call gravity.

b) The confirmation that planets in the solar system are in orbit around the Sun, not the Earth.

c) The discovery that some comets return at regular intervals.

d) The development of the atomic theory.

e) The theory of plate tectonics.

f) The discovery of any one chemical element.

g) The first use of vaccination.

h) The discovery of penicillin and its effects on bacteria.

4 To answer this question you will need to carry out your own research by studying relevant books.

a) The ancient poet Virgil said that bees were 'bred' in the putrefying entrails of a young bull.

i) Where did he believe the bees had come from?

ii) What does 'spontaneous generation' mean?

b) Van Helmont (1577–1644) stated that 'The emanations arising from the bottoms of marshes bring forth frogs, leeches, herbs and a good many other things.' What was his recipe for creating mice?

c) In the seventeenth century the Italian Francesco Redi carried out a simple experiment which shook the accepted belief in spontaneous generation. Describe this experiment.

d) What discovery did Anton van Leeuwenhoek (1632–1723) make using his newly invented microscope, and how did this revive belief in spontaneous generation?

e) Louis Pasteur predicted that the microbes which caused broth to decay came from the air and did not arise spontaneously. Describe the experiments he carried out to test his predictions.

f) i) What were the first simple forms of life?

  ii) How are they believed to have formed in the primaeval oceans?

  iii) Is this an example of spontaneous generation?

7.1.2 Scientific Method

1 Read the following passage, then answer the questions which follow.

The Rotation Period of Mercury – a Sad Scientific Saga

Even in the best possible observing conditions, it is difficult to see surface markings on the planet Mercury using a telescope. Fuzzy drawings showing some details were first published at the beginning of the nineteenth century. These were used by the German scientist Friedrich Bessel, who calculated that the rotation period of Mercury was exactly 24 hours. This value is very similar to the known rotation periods of Earth and Mars, which also rotate once in approximately 24 hours.

Bessel's value was accepted for many years, until the Italian astronomer Giovanni Schiaparelli made some new observations of Mercury. He decided that the rotation period was 88 days, exactly the same length of time that it takes Mercury to complete one orbit of the Sun. This meant that Mercury would keep one side facing the Sun all the time, just as the Moon always keeps the same side facing Earth.

Schiaparelli's value for the rotation period of Mercury was accepted as correct by scientists for over 70 years. In 1962, American scientists showed (using radio astronomy) that there was no great difference in temperature between the 'day' and 'night' sides of Mercury. This was very difficult to explain if Schiaparelli was correct. Instead of rejecting Schiaparelli's value, astronomers suggested that Mercury must have a thin, invisible atmosphere, which circulates and carries warmth to the 'night' side. This theory survived until 1965, when another team of American scientists showed conclusively using radar that Mercury's rotation period was 58.6 days.

Adapted from The Planets *by Peter Francis.*

a) Briefly explain how observing the surface features of a planet can be used to calculate its rotation period.

b) Some of the scientists mentioned in the passage did not rely on observations alone in making their decisions, partly because it was difficult to obtain accurate drawings of Mercury. What *other* factors probably influenced the following decisions?

i) Bessel concluded that Mercury rotated once in 24 hours.

ii) Schiaparelli concluded that Mercury rotated once in 88 days.

c) Explain why the lack of any difference in surface temperature between the day and night sides of Mercury conflicted with Schiaparelli's value of the rotation period.

d) The scientific community is sometimes slow to accept new ideas in all branches of science.

i) Give *one* example of this from the passage.

ii) Write down *one* advantage and *one* disadvantage of this resistance to change.

2 A formula known as 'Bode's law' gives a reasonably good prediction of the distance of some of the planets from the Sun. The 'law' can be expressed as a series of numbers, which are changed according to the rules of the law, as shown below.

1. Start with the numbers 0 and 3, then keep multiplying by 2 to obtain the next number in the series.

   0, 3, 6, 12, . . .

2. Add 4 to each number.

   4, 7, 10, 16, . . .

3. Divide each number by 10.

   0.4, 0.7, 1.0, 1.6, . . .

This series of numbers is very close to the distances of the planets from the Sun, expressed as multiples of the Sun–Earth distance (known as an astronomical unit):

Planet	Distance from the Sun (astronomical units)	Distance as predicted by Bode's law
Mercury	0.39	0.4
Venus	0.72	0.7
Earth	1.00	1.0
Mars	1.52	1.6

a) What is the difference between a law and a theory?

b) Use Bode's law to predict the distance from the Sun of a further *six* planets beyond Mars.

c) Which of your answers to part b) match up well with the distances to the remaining objects in the inner solar system?

Object	Distance from the Sun (astronomical units)
Asteroids (e.g. Ceres)	2.8
Jupiter	5.2
Saturn	9.5
Uranus	19.2
Neptune	30.0
Pluto	39.4

d) Write down *one* reason why somebody might believe that Bode's law is a valid, physical law.

e) Give *two* points which could be used to argue that Bode's law is just a coincidence.

3 a) The following passage describes how scientists work. Copy and complete the passage, choosing the correct word from the list below. Some words may be chosen more than once.

> materials   investigation   rejected   facts   knowledge
> books   modified   theory   hypothesis   forces
> predictions   experiments

Scientists are interested in explaining how the _____ of nature operate and how _____ behave. During an _____ they discover new _____, which they try to understand by devising a _____. If this is successful and its _____ turn out to be correct, then the _____ becomes a _____. Further _____ they carry out may reveal new _____ which the _____ cannot explain – it must then be _____, or _____ completely in favour of an alternative. Some time later, these ideas may appear in _____ as part of the body of _____ in science.

b) Explain why it is not possible to prove a scientific theory beyond all doubt.

4 The caloric theory states that heat is an invisible fluid which can flow from a hot body to a cold one.

a) Write down *one* method of heating an object which can be understood using the caloric theory.

b) Write down *one* method of heating an object which cannot be understood using the caloric theory.

c) Which theory has replaced the caloric theory? How does it help to understand your answer to part b)?

5　Science makes use of models to help us to understand ideas which are not part of our everyday experience.

a)　Two models of the atom are shown below.

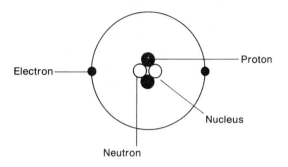

Electron ——

Proton

Nucleus

Neutron

Model 1

spherical, electrically neutral, no internal structure

Model 2

spherical, with a small positively charged nucleus surrounded by negative electrons

How successful is each of the models in explaining the following?

　i) diffusion

　ii) a chemical reaction

　iii) radioactivity

b)　i) Describe the lock and key model of enzyme action.

　　ii) Enzymes are active within a narrow temperature range, are very specific, and operate at low concentrations. Which of these properties is (are) explained by the model? Explain your choice(s).

6　Which of the following advertising claims could be tested scientifically? Explain your choice in each case.

a)　'You will get more miles per gallon by changing to OSSO petrol'

b)　'Tube for tube, DENTOCREAM contains more fluoride than INFRABRITE'

c)　'TOPERADE is probably the best alcohol-free lager on Earth'

d)　'NOSMOKE solid fuel produces more energy per kilogramme than COALACE'

e)　'ZAD washes whiter than SERF'

7   'Scientific research should not be allowed to take place if there is a danger that the resulting knowledge could be used in a harmful way'.

Give your opinion of this view, mentioning each of the following areas of scientific research in your account:

Poisons
Nuclear power
Bacteria and viruses
Genetic engineering
Embryo research